BRIEF NUMERICAL METHODS

PRENTICE-HALL APPLIED MATHEMATICS SERIES

PRENTICE-HALL INTERNATIONAL, INC., *London*
PRENTICE-HALL OF AUSTRALIA, PTY. LTD., *Sydney*
PRENTICE-HALL OF CANADA, LTD., *Toronto*
PRENTICE-HALL OF INDIA (PRIVATE), LTD., *New Delhi*
PRENTICE-HALL OF JAPAN, INC., *Tokyo*

BRIEF NUMERICAL METHODS

WENDELL E. GROVE

Associate Professor of Mathematics
General Motors Institute

PRENTICE-HALL, INC.

ENGLEWOOD CLIFFS, N. J.

Library of Congress Catalog Card No. 66-22080

Printed in the United States of America
08291-C

PREFACE

The growth of the use of digital computers in all aspects of science and engineering requires that engineers and scientists have a knowledge of the impact of digital computers on their professions. The material presented in the following pages is an attempt to acquaint students of these disciplines with some of the elementary numerical methods found useful in the field of computing. The text originated as the basis of a three hour per week, twelve week semester course in numerical methods at General Motors Institute. The material can be presented to students concurrently with a beginning course in differential equations.

The student should program a large variety of the methods included in the problem sections at the end of each chapter. I have frequently assigned one problem to each student and have had him program it by various methods. Of course, many of the problems may be done with a desk calculator, but this is senseless drudgery if a computer with an algebraic compiler such as Fortran is available. At General Motors Institute we currently have an IBM 1620 Model II computer with 40000 decimal digit core storage. This machine is capable of handling FORGO, which is a load and go version of Fortran developed at the University of Wisconsin. The complete diagnostics of this system have proven to be very useful to beginning computer and numerical methods students. For large problems we use Fortran II.

I wish to thank the General Motors Institute Computer Services and Miss Laura Steele for their friendly cooperation with my students and myself in solving our problems. In addition I wish to give credit to Assistant Professor R. W. Brown and Associate Professors D. D. McKeachie and O. T. McMillan for their helpful comments. In particular I would like to credit Professor M. L. DeMoss for pushing me into writing the material and to acknowledge gratefully the criticism of the manuscript made by my father, Professor V. G. Grove of Michigan State University. For typing the manuscript, I wish to thank Mrs. Frances Abel. And I owe a large vote of thanks to my wife for her proofreading ability and her considerable patience with me.

WENDELL E. GROVE

CONTENTS

to my father

1 ITERATIVE SOLUTION OF ALGEBRAIC AND TRANSCENDENTAL EQUATIONS

1.1 INTRODUCTION

The solution of some equations may be obtained by direct methods. A direct method is one which will produce an exact answer after a finite number of operations. The solution of the quadratic equation by the quadratic formula is an example of a direct method. Even here the answer may be irrational and it cannot be written down exactly but only to a finite number of figures. There are direct methods for cubic and quartic equations also. However, direct methods may not be the most desirable for computer calculations because of round-off and propagation errors which often compound themselves.

Another approach is an approximation technique such as Horner's method for polynomial equations. This method uses a starting guess and successively improves on it with a repetition of similar steps. This is an iterative technique. Iterative techniques are useful in programming digital computers for two important reasons:

(1) The use of the same set of instructions repetitively saves space in the computer's memory.

(2) The round-off errors made are minimized, whereas in direct methods they compound themselves.

Horner's method is not used in computing, for it is designed for hand calculation. Each multiplication involves a multidigit number and a single-digit number. The digital computer can handle numbers with large numbers of digits just as easily as single digits and, therefore, the method has no advantages over other methods requiring more arithmetic of a nature repugnant to human calculators but easily handled by a digital computer.

1

1.2 A PROCESS FOR SQUARE ROOT

Now let us consider an iterative technique for finding the square root of a positive real number $A > 1$. Let X_0 be our first guess. Now compute A/X_0. If $A/X_0 = X_0$ we are done because $X_0^2 = A$. The probability that this will occur is very remote. Suppose that $A/X_0 < X_0$ and now $A < X_0^2$ and the guess X_0 is too large. If X_0 is too large $A/X_0 < \sqrt{A}$. Thus X_0 is too large and A/X_0 is too small. That is,

$$\frac{A}{X_0} < \sqrt{A} < X_0$$

Similarly we can establish that if $A/X_0 > X_0$ then $X_0 < \sqrt{A}$ and $X_0 < \sqrt{A} < A/X_0$. In either case ($X_0 > \sqrt{A}$ or $X_0 < \sqrt{A}$) the square root of A is between A/X_0 and X_0. As a trial let us guess again: $X_1 = \frac{1}{2}[X_0 + (A/X_0)]$. This average at least appears reasonable. Later on we will show a derivation of this method. For the present we will assume it will converge to $\sqrt{A}$ as we use it repetitively or, in other words, iterate the formula.

EXAMPLE. Find $\sqrt{72}$ using $X_0 = 1$ and $X_{n+1} = \frac{1}{2}[X_n + (A/X_n)]$.

$$X_1 = \frac{1}{2}\left(1 + \frac{72}{1}\right) = 36.5$$

$$X_2 = \frac{1}{2}\left(36.5 + \frac{72}{36.5}\right) = 19.236$$

$$X_3 = \frac{1}{2}\left(19.236 + \frac{72}{19.236}\right) = 11.4896$$

$$X_4 = 8.8780710$$

$$X_5 = 8.4939705$$

$$X_6 = 8.4852860$$

$$X_7 = 8.4852815$$

The last approximation, X_7, is accurate to six significant figures.

A frequently used starting value for $\sqrt{A}$ is $X_0 = A/2$. For $\sqrt{72}$ this yields the following:

$$X_1 = \frac{1}{2}\left(36 + \frac{72}{36}\right) = 19$$

$$X_2 = \frac{1}{2}\left(19 + \frac{72}{19}\right) = 11.39$$

$$X_3 = \frac{1}{2}\left(11.39 + \frac{72}{11.39}\right) = 8.88567$$

$$X_4 = 8.493707$$

$$X_5 = 8.48528$$

$$X_6 = 8.485281 \qquad \text{accurate to six figures in six iterations.}$$

So far we have no guarantee that this will converge to the root in all cases. This we will observe in the next section. The above method has frequently been programmed as a subroutine on digital computers.

Useful iterative methods should have the following requirements:

(1) A means of making a satisfactory first guess. In many applications physical or other considerations may provide this guess.

(2) A means of systematically improving on the previous approximations.

(3) A criterion (or choice of several criteria) for stopping the iteration when sufficient accuracy has been obtained.

Iterative techniques are important and frequently used in the solution of ordinary and partial differential equations, simultaneous linear equations, and simultaneous nonlinear equations. This chapter will be limited to a discussion of iterative methods used in the solution of algebraic and transcendental equations.

1.3 THE ITERATIVE FORM $x = f(x)$

In this chapter we will use the following notation: When considering a function equated to zero we will write $F(x) = 0$, and when the function is equated to x by suitable manipulation we will write $x = f(x)$. That is,

$$F(x) = x^3 - 9x + 1 = 0 \qquad \text{or} \qquad x = \frac{x^3 + 1}{9}$$

where

$$\frac{x^3 + 1}{9} = f(x).$$

(Other formulations are possible.) The square-root problem was of this form, $x = f(x)$. Now we will consider when such a form will result in convergence to a root.

The mean value theorem: *If $f(x)$ is continuous $a \le x \le b$ and $f'(x)$ is continuous $a < x < b$ then $f(b) - f(a) = f'(\xi)(b - a)$ where $a < \xi < b$.* Any standard calculus text can be consulted for the proof of this theorem.

Consider the equation $F(x) = 0$. We change the equation into the form $x = f(x)$ and start to guess at a solution. Let x_0 be this guess. Now

$$x_1 = f(x_0)$$
$$x_2 = f(x_1)$$
.
.
.
$$x_{n+1} = f(x_n)$$

Apply the mean value theorem:

$$f(x_n) - f(x_{n-1}) = f'(\xi_n)(x_n - x_{n-1})$$

where ξ_n is between x_n and x_{n-1}.

Since $x_{n+1} = f(x_n)$, we have

$$x_{n+1} - x_n = f'(\xi_n)(x_n - x_{n-1})$$

Hence

$$|x_{n+1} - x_n| = |f'(\xi_n)| \, |(x_n - x_{n-1})|$$
$$|x_n - x_{n-1}| = |f'(\xi_{n-1})| \, |(x_{n-1} - x_{n-2})|$$
$$|x_{n-1} - x_{n-2}| = |f'(\xi_{n-2})| \, |(x_{n-2} - x_{n-3})|$$
.
.
$$|x_3 - x_2| = |f'(\xi_2)| \, |(x_2 - x_1)|$$
$$|x_2 - x_1| = |f'(\xi_1)| \, |(x_1 - x_0)|$$

Now suppose that $f'(x)$ is bounded. That is, $|f'(x)| \leq M$ for all x in the range indicated. Replace $|f'(\xi_n)|$ by M so that

$$|x_{n+1} - x_n| \leq M|x_n - x_{n-1}|$$
$$|x_n - x_{n-1}| \leq M|x_{n-1} - x_{n-2}|$$
$$|x_{n-1} - x_{n-2}| \leq M|x_{n-2} - x_{n-3}|$$
.
.
$$|x_3 - x_2| \leq M|x_2 - x_1|$$
$$|x_2 - x_1| \leq M|x_1 - x_0|$$

Multiplying all these inequalities and simplifying, we obtain:

$$|x_{n+1} - x_n| \leq M^n|x_1 - x_0|.$$

If the iteration is to converge, then $\lim_{n\to\infty} |x_{n+1} - x_n| = 0$. This condition is forced if $M < 1$. Since $|f'(x)| \leq M$, a condition sufficient for convergence is that $|f'(x)| < 1$ where our x_i are in the interval where this condition exists.

If the slope is very small in absolute value when compared to one, the convergence is quite rapid. If the slope in absolute value is close to one, the convergence is very slow.

Let us consider the previous example. For the square root

$$x_{n+1} = \frac{1}{2}\left(x_n + \frac{A}{x_n}\right).$$

In the pattern $x = f(x)$

$$f(x) = \frac{1}{2}\left(x + \frac{A}{x}\right)$$

$$f'(x) = \frac{1}{2}\left(1 - \frac{A}{x^2}\right)$$

We observe that for any x in the neighborhood of $\sqrt{A}$, $|f'(x)| < 1$ so convergence is assured. For $x_{n+1} = 20 \log x_n$

$$f(x) = 20 \log x$$

$$f'(x) = \frac{20 \log e}{x} = \frac{8.6860}{x}$$

This slope is also less than one but does not approach zero as we converge to the solution. Hence convergence is slower.

The following geometric construction emphasizes the fact that the necessary and sufficient condition for convergence of $x = f(x)$ is that the absolute value of $f'(x)$ be less than one.

The construction is done in this manner. Plot both $y = x$ and $y = f(x)$. The value of x where these cross is a solution of the equation $x = f(x)$. In the first example $0 < f'(x) < 1$ (Fig. 1.1). For a given x_0 on the x-axis, the

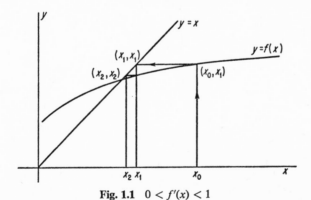

Fig. 1.1 $0 < f'(x) < 1$

ordinate of the curve $y = f(x)$ is $f(x_0)$. If one moves horizontally from $[x_0, f(x_0)]$ to the line $y = x$, that point has coordinates (x_1, x_1). From there one goes vertically to the curve $y = f(x)$. This point is (x_1, x_2). If the pattern of movement is continued one converges to the solution in this case.

From the above it appears that if $0 < f'(x) < 1$ an iteration of the type $x_{n+1} = f(x_n)$ converges monotonically to the required solution. If

$-1 < f'(x) < 0$, it converges in an oscillating manner (Fig. 1.2). Further, if $f'(x) > 1$, the iteration $x_{n+1} = f(x_n)$ diverges monotonically (Fig. 1.3). If $f'(x) < -1$, the iteration diverges in an oscillating manner (Fig. 1.4).

The preceding facts should be considered when setting up an iterative solution of a problem where more than one choice is available. In the example $x = 20 \log_{10} x$ it is clear that the alternate relationship $x = 10^{.05x}$

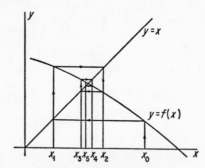

Fig. 1.2 Oscillating convergence.
$$-1 < f'(x) < 0$$

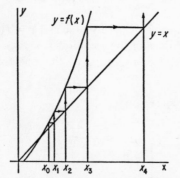

Fig. 1.3 Monotonic divergence.
$$f'(x) > 1$$

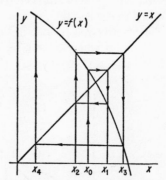

Fig. 1.4 Oscillating divergence.
$$f'(x) < -1$$

would not converge since $(d/dx)(10^{.05x}) = 10^{.05x} \ln 10(.05)$ is greater than one in the neighborhood of 30. In the case of the equation $x^3 - x + 12 = 0$, a setup of the form $x = (x - 12)/x^2$ would more likely converge than $x = x^3 + 12$.

1.4 ORDER OF ITERATION

Let us now consider other characteristics which influence the rate of convergence of an iteration of the form $x = f(x)$. We have already indicated that the value of $f'(x)$ in the neighborhood of the root may be used to prove convergence or divergence.

Let ε_n be the departure of the nth iterate from the true solution $\bar{x}$. Let us use $x_n = \bar{x} + \varepsilon_n$ so that ε_n is the error in the nth approximation. Let us now expand $f(x)$ in a Taylor series about $\bar{x}$. In general

$$f(x) = f(\bar{x}) + f'(\bar{x})(x - \bar{x}) + \frac{f''(\bar{x})(x - \bar{x})^2}{2!} + \frac{f'''(\bar{x})(x - \bar{x})^3}{3!} + \cdots$$

In particular if we put x_n for x and $x_n - \bar{x} = \varepsilon_n$

$$f(x_n) = f(\bar{x}) + f'(\bar{x})\varepsilon_n + \frac{f''(\bar{x})\varepsilon_n^2}{2!} + \frac{f'''(\bar{x})\varepsilon_n^3}{3!} + \cdots$$

Since $f(x_n) = x_{n+1}$ and $f(\bar{x}) = \bar{x}$ then

$$x_{n+1} = \bar{x} + f'(\bar{x})\varepsilon_n + \frac{f''(\bar{x})\varepsilon_n^2}{2!} + \frac{f'''(\bar{x})\varepsilon_n^3}{3!} + \cdots$$

or

$$x_{n+1} - \bar{x} = f'(\bar{x})\varepsilon_n + \frac{f''(\bar{x})\varepsilon_n^2}{2!} + \frac{f'''(\bar{x})\varepsilon_n^3}{3!} + \cdots$$

Since $x_{n+1} - \bar{x} = \varepsilon_{n+1}$, then

$$\varepsilon_{n+1} = f'(\bar{x})\varepsilon_n + \frac{f''(\bar{x})\varepsilon_n^2}{2!} + \frac{f'''(\bar{x})\varepsilon_n^3}{3!} + \cdots$$

We have now the $(n + 1)$st iterate expressed in terms of a series involving the nth iterate and the several derivatives of $f(x)$ at the solution. If the nth iterate is a fair approximation of $\bar{x}$, then ε_n should be small and the series should converge. If the first term of the series were missing, i.e., $f'(\bar{x}) = 0$, the series should converge even more rapidly. If both $f'(\bar{x})$ and $f''(\bar{x})$ are zero, convergence should be greatly accelerated. We are now prepared to define "order of iteration."

Definition: *The order of an iteration $x = f(x)$ is the order of the lowest order nonzero derivative of $f(x)$ at the solution.**

In the square-root problem

$$x_{n+1} = \frac{1}{2}\left(x_n + \frac{A}{x_n}\right)$$

$$f(x) = \frac{1}{2}\left(x + \frac{A}{x}\right)$$

---

* For non-integral order of iteration, we may use

$$0 < \lim_{n \to \infty} \left|\frac{\varepsilon_{n+1}}{(\varepsilon^n)^p}\right| < \infty$$

where p is the order of iteration and ε_n is the error after n iterations.

$$f'(x) = \frac{1}{2}\left(1 - \frac{A}{x^2}\right)$$

$$f''(x) = \frac{A}{x^3}$$

Since $\bar{x} = \sqrt{A}$,

$$f'(\sqrt{A}) = \frac{1}{2}\left(1 - \frac{A}{A}\right) = 0$$

$$f''(\sqrt{A}) = \frac{A}{(\sqrt{A})^3} = \frac{1}{\sqrt{A}} \neq 0$$

Hence this is a second-order iteration.

In the example $x = 20 \log x$ none of the derivatives is zero for any finite x. This is then a first-order iteration.

1.5 SIMPLE ITERATION FLOW CHART

Note: The use of the equals sign in flow charts must be interpreted as the Fortran use of the equals sign. That is, $X_A = X_B$ implies that the current value of X_B will replace the value of X_A.

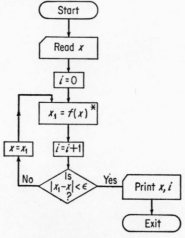

Fig. 1.5.

The flow chart given here (Fig. 1.5) is suitable for Newton-Raphson method if the box labeled (*) is replaced by

$$x_1 = x - \frac{F(x)}{F'(x)}$$

1.6 THE NEWTON-RAPHSON METHOD

Suppose we are to solve an equation of the form $F(x) = 0$. Referring to Fig. 1.6, we can derive the following method:

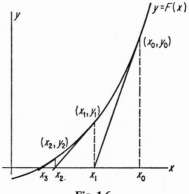

If we plot $y = F(x)$, the value of x that makes $y = 0$ is the solution of $F(x) = 0$. If our starting guess is x_0 from point (x_0, y_0) on the curve, we draw a tangent to the curve. The point where this crosses the x-axis should be an improvement over x_0. We call this x_1 and repeat the cycle until our solution is sufficiently accurate.

To accomplish the above analytically we can write the equation of the tangent line to the curve at (x_0, y_0) using the point

Fig. 1.6.

slope form $y - y_0 = (x - x_0)F'(x_0)$.

The second value of x, x_1, is the value that makes the y of this line equal to zero. Substituting $y_0 = F(x_0)$, we get

$$0 - F(x_0) = (x_1 - x_0)F'(x_0)$$

$$-\frac{F(x_0)}{F'(x_0)} = x_1 - x_0$$

$$x_1 = x_0 - \frac{F(x_0)}{F'(x_0)}$$

In general

$$x_{n+1} = x_n - \frac{F(x_n)}{F'(x_n)}$$

This is called the Newton-Raphson formula. It has been the most widely used of all iteration formulas.

Let us now apply the Newton-Raphson method to the solution of $x^2 - A = 0$. Here

$$F(x) = x^2 - A$$

$$F'(x) = 2x$$

$$x_{n+1} = x_n - \frac{x_n^2 - A}{2x_n} = \frac{1}{2}\left[\frac{2x_n^2 - x_n^2 + A}{x_n}\right] = \frac{1}{2}\left[x_n + \frac{A}{x_n}\right]$$

We observe that this is the square-root formula that we devised earlier.

Notation. A word about notation seems appropriate here. If we are using an iteration of the form $x = f(x)$ or $x = f(x, y, z)$, we shall use the small letter f for the function. On the other hand, if we are solving equations

$F(x) = 0$ or systems of equations $F(x, y) = 0$, $G(x, y) = 0$, we shall always use the capital letters for the functions.

Before considering a numerical example let us examine the order of an iteration of the Newton-Raphson type. We previously observed that in the square-root problem the iteration we devised was second-order. Also we have shown that the Newton-Raphson method gives the same formula. Hence it might be assumed that the Newton-Raphson is a second-order process.

Consider

$$x_{n+1} = x_n - \frac{F(x_n)}{F'(x_n)}$$

where $F(x) = 0$ has only simple roots.

For an iteration of the type $x = f(x)$, here

$$f(x) = x - \frac{F(x)}{F'(x)}$$

$$f'(x) = 1 - \frac{F'(x)F'(x) - F(x)F''(x)}{[F'(x)]^2}$$

$$= \frac{[F'(x)]^2 - [F'(x)]^2 + F(x)F''(x)}{[F'(x)]^2} = \frac{F(x)F''(x)}{[F'(x)]^2}$$

At the solution

$$x = \bar{x}, F(\bar{x}) = 0.$$

Hence $f'(\bar{x}) = 0$ and the iteration is at least second-order. We leave it to the reader to show that at the solution

$$f''(\bar{x}) = \frac{F''(\bar{x})}{F'(\bar{x})}$$

Since this is the case and $F''(\bar{x})$ is not in general zero, it follows that the Newton-Raphson method is a second-order process for simple roots.

The Newton-Raphson method is first-order for roots of multiplicity n for $n > 1$.

Let our equation be $G(x) = (x - a)^n F(x) = 0$ where $x = a$ is a root of multiplicity n.

The Newton-Raphson method is now

$$x_{i+1} = x_i - \frac{(x_i - a)^n F(x_i)}{n(x_i - a)^{n-1}F(x_i) + (x_i - a)^n F'(x_i)}$$

Consider the function

$$N(x) = x - \frac{(x - a)^n F(x)}{n(x - a)^{n-1}F(x) + (x - a)^n F'(x)}$$

or

$$N(x) = x - \frac{(x - a)F(x)}{nF(x) + (x - a)F'(x)}$$

Recalling the definition of order of an iteration we write

$$N'(x) =$$
$$1 - \frac{[nF(x)+(x-a)F'(x)][F(x)+(x-a)F'(x)]-(x-a)F(x)[nF'(x)+F'(x)+(x-a)F''(x)]}{[nF(x)+(x-a)F'(x)]^2}$$

Recalling that $x = a$ is a root of $(x - a)^n G(x) = 0$ and simplifying,

$$N'(a) = 1 - \frac{nF(a) \cdot F(a)}{[nF(a)]^2} = 1 - \frac{1}{n}$$

and, since $N'(a) = F''(a) \neq 0$, the Newton-Raphson method is first-order for roots of multiplicity n, $n > 1$. Note that if $n = 1$, $N'(a) = 0$ and we have the previous result.

EXAMPLE 1.   Solve $x^3 - 4x + 1 = 0$.

Solution. A plot of $y = x^3 - 4x + 1$ shows that the equation $x^3 - 4x + 1 = 0$ has roots between -3 and -2, 0 and 1, and 1 and 2. Let us first find the larger root.

$$F(x) = x^3 - 4x + 1$$

$$F'(x) = 3x^2 - 4$$

Using $x_0 = 2$, $F(2) = 2^3 - 4(2) + 1 = 1$

$$F'(2) = 3(2^2) - 4 = 8$$

$$x_1 = x_0 - \frac{F(x_0)}{F'(x_0)} = 2 - \frac{1}{8} = 1.875$$

$$x_2 = 1.863$$

$$x_3 = 1.863$$

Using $x_0 = 0$, $F(0) = 1$

$$F'(0) = -4$$

$$x_1 = 0 - \frac{1}{-4} = .25$$

$$x_2 = .25 + .0041 = .2541$$

$$x_3 = .2541$$

Using $x_0 = -3$, $F(-3) = 16$

$$F'(-3) = 23$$

$$x_1 = -2.305$$

$$x_2 = -2.038$$

$$x_3 = -2.116$$

$$x_4 = -2.116$$

Since this is one type of problem that can be solved using a direct method, let us solve this using a standard method for cubics. The equation $x^3 + ax + b = 0$ where $b^2/4 + a^3/27 < 0$ has as solutions

$$x_k = \pm 2 \sqrt{\frac{-a}{3}} \cos\left(\frac{\phi}{3} + 120°k\right), \qquad k = 0, 1, 2$$

where

$$\cos \phi = \sqrt{\frac{b^2}{4} \div \frac{(-a)^3}{27}}$$

In our example $a = -4$, $b = 1$,

$$\cos \phi = \sqrt{\frac{\frac{1}{4}}{4^3/27}} = \frac{\sqrt{27}}{16} = \frac{3\sqrt{3}}{16}$$

$$\phi = 71.04°$$

Since $b > 0$ we use the negative sign and $\phi/3 = 23.7°$.

$$x_0 = -\frac{4}{\sqrt{3}} \cos 23.7° = -2.12$$

$$x_1 = -\frac{4}{\sqrt{3}} \cos 143.7° = +\frac{4}{\sqrt{3}} \cos 36.3° = 1.86$$

$$x_2 = -\frac{4}{\sqrt{3}} \cos 263.7° = +\frac{4}{\sqrt{3}} \cos 83.7° = +.254$$

These calculations were done with a slide rule. Although the solution is straightforward, it should be fairly apparent that this method would be difficult to use in a computer program. In addition it will, of course, only solve cubic equations.

EXAMPLE 2.   Use the Newton-Raphson formula to solve $F(x) = \log_{10} x - .05x = 0$.

Solution.

$$F(x) = \log_{10} x - .05x$$

$$F'(x) = \frac{.434294}{x} - .05$$

$$x_{n+1} = x_n - \frac{\log_{10} x_n - .05x_n}{(.434294/x_n) - .05} = x_n \left(\frac{.434294 - \log_{10} x_n}{.434294 - .05x_n}\right)$$

Using

$$x_0 = 30$$
$$x_1 = 29.356$$
$$x_2 = 29.353$$
$$x_3 = 29.353$$

Note that this converges much more rapidly than the simple iteration solution of the same equation.

In many problems involving simple functions, the expression for the derivative is easily obtained. Coding such a problem for solution with a digital computer is then quite easy. When the function $F(x)$ is such that its derivative may not be readily written down or is such that it is very complex, an approximation for $F'(x)$ may be used. By definition

$$F'(x) = \lim_{\Delta x \to 0} \frac{F(x + \Delta x) - F(x)}{\Delta x}$$

One can use as an approximation for $F'(x)$ the expression

$$\frac{F(x + \Delta x) - F(x)^*}{\Delta x}$$

Care needs to be used in the selection of the increment Δx. If Δx is too small, the influence of round-off error may become magnified. If Δx is too large and the radius of curvature small, there is danger that the approximate value of $F'(x)$ will not be good. Generally in computer work a Δx of the order of $.0001x$ is used. This may be varied to fit the individual problem.

In a hand calculation where $F'(x)$ and $F''(x)$ can be easily computed and a root is known to exist between $x = a$ and $x = b$, the value such that $F(x)$ and $F''(x)$ have the same sign is taken for x_0. It is left to the reader to show graphically that this will give the more rapid convergence.

It should be said that if the function $F(x)$ is such that $F''(x)$ has a change in sign in the neighborhood of a root, the Newton-Raphson may not converge. This may be seen graphically from Fig. 1.7. Also if $F'(x)$ is considerably less than one numerically, small variation in the computed slope will give large variations in the computed value of the next x. The method works best when the numerical values of the slope are large.

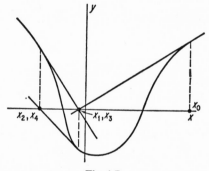

Fig. 1.7.

The Newton-Raphson method may converge to a root which is not the desired root. In many physical problems the root may be known to have certain characteristics, perhaps it is known to be positive. A critical look

---

* Another approximation for $F'(x)$ is

$$F'(x) \approx \frac{F(x + \Delta x) - F(x - \Delta x)}{2\Delta x}$$

at Fig. 1.7 will convince us to be wary when using the Newton-Raphson method.

An alternative approach to the Newton-Raphson method is to expand $F(x)$ as a Taylor series about x_0 and truncate the series after the first derivative term and remainder term as follows:

$$F(x) = F(x_0) + F'(x_0)(x - x_0) + \frac{F''(\xi)(x - x_0)^2}{2!}$$

Let $\bar{x}$ be a root and x_1 the first approximation

$$F(x_1) = F(x_0) + F'(x_0)(x_1 - x_0) + \frac{F''(\xi)(x_1 - x_0)^2}{2!}$$

Let us assume x_1 is a good approximation to $\bar{x}$ so that $F(x_1)$ is nearly zero and the remainder is also very small. Now, replacing $F(x_1)$ by zero, we have

$$0 = F(x_0) + F'(x_0)(x_1 - x_0)$$

Solving for x_1, we have

$$x_1 = x_0 - \frac{F(x_0)}{F'(x_0)}$$

which we recall as the Newton-Raphson formula obtained from a different nongeometrical approach.

1.7 CRITERIA FOR ENDING THE ITERATION

For certain iterative methods the use of $|x_{n+1} - x_n| < \varepsilon_1$ where x_n is the nth approximation and x_{n+1} is the $(n + 1)$st approximation may lead to the termination of the iteration prematurely. If the iteration is converging very slowly, the change in one step may be very small. In such cases the use of $|f(x_n)| < \varepsilon_2$ may be desirable in conjunction with the previous notion. Figure 1.8 is a flow chart for such cases.

1.8 AITKEN'S DELTA SQUARED PROCESS

In using the simple iterative process $x = f(x)$, we use only the value of the previous x to obtain a better answer. In using the Newton-Raphson formula we used the previous x, the value of the function, and the value of its derivative at the previous x to give an improved value. This ordinarily converged more rapidly than $x = f(x)$. It would seem reasonable that if we used more than one of a set of successive approximations in an iteration of the form $x = f(x)$, we should be able to obtain a better next approximation.

Let us assume that we have three successive approximations x_k, x_{k+1}, x_{k+2} obtained using $x = f(x)$.

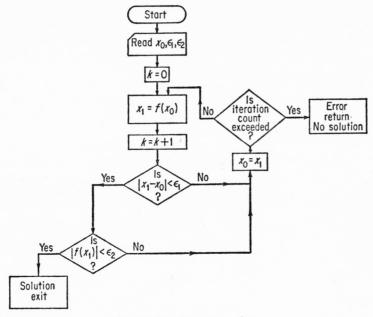

Fig. 1.8 Iteration of $x = f(x)$.

$$x_{k+1} = f(x_k)$$

$$x_{k+2} = f(x_{k+1})$$

Let $\bar{x}$ be the required solution. Using the mean value theorem,

$$f(x_k) - f(\bar{x}) = (x_k - \bar{x})f'(\xi_1)$$

where ξ_1 is between x_k and $\bar{x}$. Also

$$f(x_{k+1}) - f(\bar{x}) = (x_{k+1} - \bar{x})f'(\xi_2)$$

where ξ_2 is between x_{k+1} and $\bar{x}$. If x_{k+1} and x_k are both near $\bar{x}$, ξ_1 and ξ_2 will be close together and $f'(\xi_1)$ and $f'(\xi_2)$ should be near equality. Since $f(x_k) = x_{k+1}$, $f(x_{k+1}) = x_{k+2}$, and $f(\bar{x}) = \bar{x}$, the above equations become

$$x_{k+1} - \bar{x} = (x_k - \bar{x})f'(\xi_1) \qquad (1.1)$$

$$x_{k+2} - \bar{x} = (x_{k+1} - \bar{x})f'(\xi_2) \qquad (1.2)$$

Dividing (1.1) by (1.2), we get

$$\frac{x_{k+1} - \bar{x}}{x_{k+2} - \bar{x}} = \frac{(x_k - \bar{x})f'(\xi_1)}{(x_{k+1} - \bar{x})f'(\xi_2)} = \frac{x_k - \bar{x}}{x_{k+1} - \bar{x}}$$

assuming $f'(\xi_1) = f'(\xi_2)$. Solving the above for $\bar{x}$, we obtain

$$\bar{x} = \frac{x_k x_{k+2} - x_{k+1}^2}{x_{k+2} - 2x_{k+1} + x_k}$$

If, as assumed, $f'(\xi_1)$ were exactly equal to $f'(\xi_2)$, this would be the required solution $\bar{x}$. Since this is not the case, we have here just a better approximation of $\bar{x}$. Let us call it x'_{k+2}. We are now prepared to outline a procedure for usiug this method.

(1) Using simple iteration with a starting guess x_0, compute x_1 and x_2.

$$x_1 = f(x_0)$$
$$x_2 = f(x_1)$$

(2) Use the formula to compute x'_2.

$$x'_2 = \frac{x_0 x_2 - x_1^2}{x_2 - 2x_1 + x_0}$$

(3)
$$x_3 = f(x'_2)$$
$$x_4 = f(x_3)$$

(4)
$$x'_4 = \frac{x'_2 x_4 - x_3^2}{x_4 - 2x_3 + x'_2}$$

(5) Repeat until the required accuracy in the solution is attained.

1.9 RULE OF FALSE POSITION OR REGULI FALSI

Consider the equation $F(x) = 0$ where x_1 and x_2 are approximations to a root, $F(x)$ is continuous for $x_1 \leq x \leq x_2$, and $F(x_1) \cdot F(x_2) < 0$. (See Fig. 1.9.)

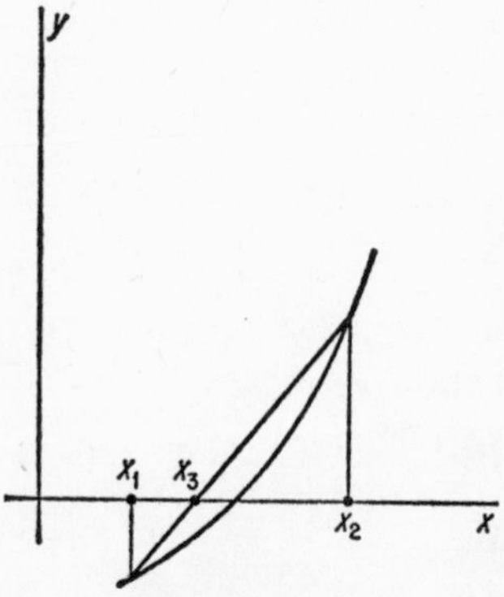

A better approximation to the root is given by

$$x_3 = \frac{x_1 F(x_2) - x_2 F(x_1)}{F(x_2) - F(x_1)}$$

This process may be iterated as

$$x_{n+1} = \frac{x_{n-1} F(x_n) - x_n F(x_{n-1})}{F(x_n) - F(x_{n-1})} \quad (1.3)$$

Formula (1.3) may be derived by drawing a line through $(x_{n-1}, F(x_{n-1}))$ and $(x_n, F(x_n))$ and using as x_{n+1} the point where this line crosses the x axis. Care should be taken to be sure that $F(x_n) \cdot F(x_{n-1}) < 0$ at each step.

Fig. 1.9.

EXAMPLE.   Solve $x^3 - 9x + 1$ by the rule of false position.

Solution.   Use $x_1 = 2$ and $x_2 = 4$, then

$$F(x_1) = (+2)^3 - 9(2) + 1 = +8 - 18 + 1 = -9$$
$$F(x_2) = (4)^3 - 9(4) + 1 = 64 - 36 + 1 = 29$$

By formula (1.90)

$$x_3 = \frac{2(29) - 4(-9)}{29 - (-9)} = \frac{58 + 36}{38} = \frac{94}{38} = 2.47368$$

$$x_4 = 2.73989$$

$$x_5 = 2.86125$$

$$x_6 = 2.91107$$

$$x_7 = 2.93816$$

$$x_8 = 2.94104$$

$$x_9 = 2.94214$$

$$x_{10} = 2.94256$$

$$x_{11} = 2.94278$$

$$x_{12} = 2.94281$$

Thus ten iterations after the initial guesses give six significant figures.
To find the root between zero and one using $x_1 = -1$ and $x_2 = 1$

$$x_3 = .125000$$

$$x_4 = .109827$$

$$x_5 = .111265$$

Here only three approximations to achieve the same precision are necessary.

1.10 SECANT METHOD

The secant method may be regarded as a modification of the Newton-Raphson method. In the Newton-Raphson method

$$x_{n+1} = x_n - \frac{F(x_n)}{F'(x_n)}$$

replace $F'(x_n)$ by the slope of the secant line between two successive approximations, as

$$m = \frac{F(x_n) - F(x_{n-1})}{x_n - x_{n-1}}$$

and now

$$x_{n+1} = x_n - \frac{F(x_n)}{m}$$

Note here that simplification of this equation yields the same equation as the rule of false position. An alternative is to use m as a constant. A choice here might be the secant line between two guesses x_1 and x_2 such that $F(x_1) \cdot F(x_2) < 0$ and $F(x)$ is continuous in the vicinity of the root. Thus pick

$$m = \frac{F(x_1) - F(x_0)}{x_1 - x_0}$$

and use this in each iteration. Convergence is very slow (of order one).

EXAMPLE. $x^3 - 9x + 1 = 0$ using $x_1 = 3$, $x_2 = 4$, and

$$x_3 = \frac{3(29) - 4(1)}{29 - 4} = \frac{83}{25} = 3.32$$

1.11 INTERVAL HALVING OR BISECTION

The method of interval halving depends on the same hypotheses as does the rule of false position. That is, to find an approximation to a root of $F(x) = 0$ we must have initial guesses x_1 and x_2 such that $F(x)$ is continuous for $x_0 \leq x \leq x_1$ and the product $F(x_0) \cdot F(x_1) < 0$. These two hypotheses guarantee that the curve $y = F(x)$ crosses the x axis between x_0 and x_1. The new approximation is

$$x_2 = \frac{x_1 + x_0}{2}$$

If $F(x_0) \cdot F(x_2) < 0$ then

$$x_3 = \frac{x_0 + x_2}{2}$$

If $F(x_1) \cdot F(x_2) < 0$ then

$$x_3 = \frac{x_1 + x_2}{2}$$

In general the new approximation is selected so that it lies in the subinterval of the previous interval which contains the root. (See Fig. 1.10.)

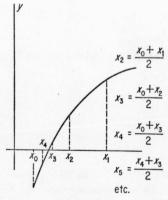

Fig. 1.10.

Note that here again convergence is slow. However, if the function is continuous, convergence is assured. In hand calculations this might not be practical to use. With a computer, where the time for one cycle is measured in thousandths or millionths of a second, there are times when it can be justified. It is to be observed that at the end of 20 iterations the interval in which the root is known to lie is reduced by a factor of 2^{-20}. Since $2^{-20} = 1/1,048,376$, in many cases 20 iterations would give the required accuracy.

EXAMPLE. Solve $x^3 - 9x + 1 = 0$ for the root between $x = 2$ and $x = 4$ by interval halving.

Solution. Since $F(x) = x^3 - 9x + 1$ is a polynomial it is continuous,

$$F(2) = -9$$
$$F(4) = 29$$

and we are now sure that a root exists between $x = 2$ and $x = 4$. Now

$$x_2 = \frac{x_0 + x_1}{2} \quad \text{or} \quad x_2 = \frac{2 + 4}{2} = 3$$

$F(3) = 1$, so the next approximation is made by checking to see that $F(2) \cdot F(3) = (-9)(1) < 0$. So

$$x_2 = 3$$
$$x_3 = 2.5$$
$$x_4 = 2.75$$
$$x_5 = 2.875$$
$$x_6 = 2.9375$$
$$x_7 = 2.96875$$
$$x_8 = 2.953125$$
$$x_9 = 2.9453125$$
$$x_{10} = 2.9414063$$
$$x_{11} = 2.9433594$$
$$x_{12} = 2.9423829$$
$$x_{13} = 2.9428712$$
$$x_{14} = 2.9427492$$
$$x_{15} = 2.9428102$$
$$x_{16} = 2.9428407$$

1.12 WEGSTEIN'S METHOD *

The Wegstein method induces convergence in some otherwise divergent iterations of the form $x = f(x)$.

* J. H. Wegstein, "Accelerating Convergence of Iterative Processes," National Bureau of Standards, Washington, D.C., ACM Communications, June 1958, pp. 9–13.

We have shown previously that an iteration of the form $x = f(x)$ will converge if $|f'(x)| < 1$ and diverges otherwise. In the development of the

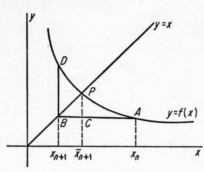

Fig. 1.11.

Wegstein formula for a function of one variable, let us consider the case where $x = f(x)$, $-1 < f'(x) < 0$ as shown in Fig. 1.11.

In this figure a better approximation for $\bar{x}$ than x_{n+1} would be a value around one-fourth greater. Let $\bar{x}_{n+1}$ be a better approximation than x_{n+1}.

Let q be the fractional part of the distance BA measured to the better approximation from x_{n+1}—that is,

$$\bar{x}_{n+1} = x_{n+1} + q(x_n - x_{n+1})$$

where

$$q = \frac{BC}{BA}$$

Rearranging,

$$\bar{x}_{n+1} = qx_n + (1 - q)x_{n+1}$$

Note that $BC = CP$.

Since

$$q = \frac{BC}{BA}$$

then

$$1 - q = \frac{CA}{BA}$$

and

$$\frac{q}{1 - q} = \frac{BC}{CA} = \frac{CP}{CA}$$

Now CP/CA is the negative of the slope of $y = f(x)$ at some point between A and P.

Let

$$\frac{q}{1 - q} = -a$$

where $a = f'(\xi_1)$ and ξ_1 is between A and P. Solving the above for q we obtain

$$q = \frac{a}{a - 1}.$$

The approximation for a that Wegstein uses is

$$a = \frac{f(x_n) - f(\bar{x}_{n-1})}{x_n - x_{n-1}}$$

which is valid for all smooth curves. If q is not important in itself to the programmer, the formula

$$\bar{x}_{n+1} = \frac{x_{n+1}\bar{x}_{n-1} - x_n\bar{x}_n}{x_n + \bar{x}_{n-1} - x_n - \bar{x}_n}$$

may be used. It may be shown that convergence by the Wegstein method is of order 1.618—that is, similar to the rate of convergence of Newton-Raphson.

Let us now outline a procedure for solving an equation of the form $x = f(x)$ using the Wegstein method. Figure 1.12 is a flow chart for this method.

(1) Use $x = f(x)$ and find

$$x_1 = f(x_0)$$
$$x_2 = f(x_1)$$

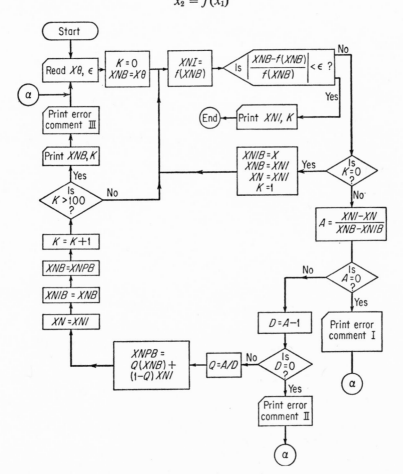

Fig. 1.12 Wegstein method.

To find $\bar{x}_2$ use

$$a = \frac{f(x_1) - f(x_0)}{x_1 - x_0} = \frac{x_2 - x_1}{x_1 - x_0}, \qquad q = \frac{a}{a - 1}$$

$$\bar{x}_2 = qx_1 + (1 - q)x_2$$

(2) Find x_3 using $x_3 = f(\bar{x}_2)$

$$a = \frac{f(\bar{x}_2) - f(x_1)}{\bar{x}_2 - x_1}, \qquad q = \frac{a}{a - 1}$$

$$\bar{x}_3 = q(\bar{x}_2) + (1 - q)x_3$$

(3) $x_4 = f(\bar{x}_3)$

$$a = \frac{x_4 - x_3}{\bar{x}_3 - \bar{x}_2}, \qquad q = \frac{a}{a - 1}$$

$$\bar{x}_4 = q\bar{x}_3 + (1 - q)x_4$$

Note that in finding $\bar{x}_{n+1}$ where $n \geq 3$

$$a = \frac{x_{n+1} - x_n}{\bar{x}_n - \bar{x}_{n-1}}$$

and

$$\bar{x}_{n+1} = q\bar{x}_n + (1 - q)x_{n+1}$$

There are not enough $\bar{x}$'s for use up to this point.

We now consider an example where $f'(x) \gg 1$ in the neighborhood of the solution.

EXAMPLE.   Solve $F(x) = x^2 - 4 = 0$ using $x = x + x^2 - 4$ and $x_0 = 6$.

Solution.

$$x_1 = 6 + 36 - 4 = 38$$

$$x_2 = 1478$$

$$a = \frac{1478 - 38}{38 - 6} = 45$$

$$q = \frac{45}{44} = 1.0227273$$

$$\bar{x}_2 = \frac{45}{44}(38) + \left(1 - \frac{45}{44}\right)(1478) = 5.272688$$

$$x_3 = f(\bar{x}_2) = 29.073927$$

$$a = \frac{f(\bar{x}_2) - f(x_1)}{\bar{x}_2 - x_1} = \frac{29.073927 - 1478}{5.272688 - 38} = 44.312$$

$$q = \frac{a}{a - 1} = 1.0231$$

$$\bar{x}_3 = 4.7226580$$

$$x_4 = f(\bar{x}_3) = 23.026157$$
$$x_5 = 7.251968$$
$$x_6 = 3.6954468$$
$$x_7 = 2.2756761$$

$$x_8 = 2.0198933 \qquad q_8 = 1.2286599$$
$$x_9 = 2.0002670 \qquad q_9 = 1.2463955$$
$$x_{10} = 2.0000005 \qquad q_{10} = 1.2497485$$

Note that convergence is slow but that the iteration does converge.

EXAMPLE. Solve $x^3 - 10x + 1 = 0$.

Solution. Set up basic iteration in the form $x = x^3 - 9x + 1$ and apply Wegstein technique with $x_1 = 6$.

$$x_1 = 5.8530200 \qquad q_1 = 1.000036$$
$$x_2 = 5.8478299 \qquad q_2 = 1.0000363$$
$$x_3 = 4.3102767 \qquad q_3 = 1.0107898$$
$$x_4 = 3.7516588 \qquad q_4 = 1.0147099$$
$$x_5 = 3.3321307 \qquad q_5 = 1.0257572$$
$$x_6 = 3.1632068 \qquad q_6 = 1.0361284$$
$$x_7 = 3.1161570 \qquad q_7 = 1.0461911$$
$$x_8 = 3.1111671 \qquad q_8 = 1.0510899$$
$$x_9 = 3.1110394 \qquad q_9 = 1.0523983$$

Solving the same equation $x^3 - 10x + 1 = 0$ with a very poor starting guess $x_0 = 15$, the Wegstein technique gives

$$x_1 = 3241$$
$$x_2 = 34043698000$$
$$x_3 = -4358794$$
$$x_4 = -43239931$$
$$\cdot$$
$$\cdot$$
$$\cdot$$
$$x_{18} = -8.8443980$$
$$x_{19} = -4.3839560$$
$$x_{20} = -3.3227150 \qquad q_{20} = 1.0421114$$
$$x_{21} = -3.2112591 \qquad q_{21} = 1.0465341$$
$$x_{22} = -3.2111470 \qquad q_{22} = 1.047655$$

This example demonstrates what may happen with a poor selection of a starting point. The iteration converges, but possibly to a different root than desired. This behavior is not peculiar only to this method.

Note that in each of these cases the value of q tends to some particular constant. It would seem that it should be possible to obtain a solution of a particular problem using the Wegstein formula for $\bar{x}_{k+1}$ and a suitably chosen constant q. Wegstein asserts that this is the case, and as a result of his experience lists the following ranges of optimum values for q. Using the definition of q found on page 20, one can see from the geometry in each case that these are reasonable ranges of values.

Case	Range for $f'(x)$	Range of optimum q
1. Oscillatory convergence	$-1 < f'(x) < 0$	$0 < q < .5$
2. Oscillatory divergence	$f'(x) < -1$	$.5 < q < 1$
3. Monotonic convergence	$0 < f'(x) < 1$	$q < 0$
4. Monotonic divergence	$f'(x) > 1$	$1 > q$

1.13 HALLEY'S METHOD

Recalling that we may develop the Newton-Raphson method by truncating the Taylor series expansion of $F(x)$ about a point x_n, let us now truncate the same series after second derivatives:

$$F(x) = F(x_n) + F'(x_n)(x - x_n) + \frac{F''(x_n)(x - x_n)^2}{2} \tag{1.4}$$

Now we will substitute $x = x_{n+1}$ and assume x_{n+1} is a good approximation to the root so that $F(x_{n+1})$ is nearly zero. In fact, we will call $F(x_{n+1}) = 0$.

$$0 = F(x_n) + F'(x_n)(x_{n+1} - x_n) + \frac{F''(x_n)(x_{n+1} - x_n)^2}{2} \tag{1.5}$$

Now we will solve for x_{n+1}:

$$(x_{n+1} - x_n)\left[F'(x_n) + \frac{F''(x_n)(x_{n+1} - x_n)}{2} \right] = -F(x_n)$$

$$x_{n+1} - x_n = -\frac{F(x_n)}{F'(x) + \dfrac{F''(x_n)(x_{n+1} - x_n)}{2}}$$

or

$$x_{n+1} = x_n - \frac{F(x_n)}{F'(x_n) + \dfrac{F''(x_n)(x_{n+1} - x_n)}{2}} \tag{1.6}$$

At this point we recall the Newton-Raphson formulation

$$x_{n+1} = x_n - \frac{F(x_n)}{F'(x_n)}$$

or

$$x_{n+1} - x_n = -\frac{F(x_n)}{F'(x_n)} \qquad (1.7)$$

In (1.6) we replace $x_{n+1} - x_n$ from equation (1.7) so that

$$x_{n+1} = x_n - \frac{F(x_n)}{F'(x_n) - \dfrac{F''(x_n) \cdot F(x_n)}{2F'(x_n)}} \qquad (1.8)$$

This is Halley's formula.

EXAMPLE.   Solve $x^3 - x - 10 = 0$ using $x_0 = 4$.

Solution. $F(x) = x^3 - x - 10$, $F'(x) = 3x^2 - 1$, $F''(x) = 6x$, and

$$x_{i+1} = x_i - \frac{x_i^3 - x_i - 10}{3x_i^2 - 1 - \dfrac{6x_i(x_i^3 - x_i - 10)}{2(3x_i^2 - 1)}}$$

Using $x_0 = 4$,

$$x_1 = 2.5394656$$
$$x_2 = 2.3104300$$
$$x_3 = 2.3089074$$
$$x_4 = 2.3089073$$
$$x_5 = 2.3089073$$

It appears that in the solution of cubic equations this method could very well be used along with synthetic division to obtain one real root and the reduced quadratic in a very short time.

1.14 MULLER'S METHOD

Given an equation $F(x) = 0$ for which we wish to locate a root. We require three starting points. (We may choose one and set up a routine for the computer to calculate the other two.) Let us assume the points are $(a, F(a))$, $(b, F(b))$, and $(c, F(c))$.

Now pass a parabola of the form

$$y = P(x) = Ax^2 + Bx + C \qquad (1.9)$$

through these points. The parabola intersects the x-axis at two points, say d and d'. Now we must choose one or the other as our next approximation

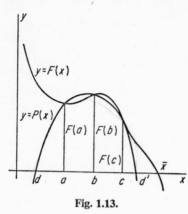

for the root $\bar{x}$. From Fig. 1.13 this is obvious, but of course it is not to the computer. We may evaluate $F(x)$ for d and d' and choose whichever causes $|F(x)|$ to be smaller. Now we use the points b, c, and d or d' (whichever was chosen) and iterate the procedure, discarding the "oldest" previous point each time.

Although we have considered this method for real roots, it is usually used to calculate complex roots. An advantage of the method is that no derivatives of the function $F(x)$ need be calculated. For real roots it is not particularly better

Fig. 1.13.

than interval halving. It does converge faster, but it requires more computations per iteration.

EXAMPLE.   Find a root of $x^3 - 14x^2 + 35x + 50 = 0$.

Solution.   Use $a = 2$, $b = 3$, $c = 4$. Now

$$F(a) = 2^3 - 14(2)^2 + 35(2) + 50 = 8 - 56 + 70 + 50 = 72$$
$$F(b) = 3^3 - 14(3)^2 + 35(3) + 50 = 27 - 126 + 105 + 50 = 56$$
$$F(c) = 4^3 - 14(4)^2 + 35(4) + 50 = 64 - 224 + 140 + 50 = 30$$

And we have the three points $(2, 72)$, $(3, 56)$ and $(4, 30)$. Using these points to fit the parabola (1.9),

$$Ax^2 + Bx + C = y$$

we obtain the three equations:

$$4A + 2B + C = 72$$
$$9A + 3B + C = 56$$
$$16A + 4B + C = 30$$

Solving these, we obtain

$$P(x) = y = -5x^2 + 9x + 74$$

Now we compute the zeros of $P(x)$ by the quadratic formula, obtaining

$$x = \frac{-9 \pm \sqrt{81 + 4(5)(74)}}{-10} = \frac{9 \pm \sqrt{1561}}{10} = \frac{9 \pm 39.5}{10}$$

or

$$x = 4.85 \quad \text{or} \quad x = -3.05$$

Evaluating $F(x)$ for these two values of x, we pick

$$x = 4.85 \qquad \text{and iterate obtaining}$$
$$x = 4.9977$$
$$x = 4.9994$$
$$x = 4.9997 \qquad \text{after four iterations}$$

PROBLEMS

1. The iteration $x_{n+1} = x_n(3A - x_n^2)/2A$ may be used to calculate $\sqrt{A}$.
   (a) Determine the order of this iteration.
   (b) Find $\sqrt{231}$ using $x_0 = 5, 10, 15$.

2. If the following is considered as an iterative form, tell what is its purpose.

$$x_{n+1} = \frac{2x_n^3 + A}{3x_n^2}$$

3. Use the formula of problem number two with $A = 425$, $x_0 = 10$.

4. The formula

$$x_{n+1} = \frac{1}{3}\frac{2x_n^2 + A}{x_n}$$

can be used to obtain the square root of A. Find the order of the iteration.

5. The formula

$$x_{n+1} = \frac{x_n(x_n^2 + 3A)}{3x_n^2 + A}$$

can be used to find the square root of A. Find the order of iteration.

6. Use the formula of problem 4 to find the square root of 425.

7. Show that the Halley's formula for the nth root of A is of order three.

The following problems are suggested for trial by simple iteration, Newton-Raphson, interval halving, rule of false position, Halley's method, the secant method, and Wegstein's method. Do not expect that all problems will work by all methods. An analysis of the problems before programming will be helpful. Try several starting values for each method, and note the number of iterations required for convergence to a specified number of figures.

8. $e^x - 3x = 0$.

9. $\tan x = \tanh x$.

10. $x^2 - \cos x = 0$.

11. $xe^x - 4 = 0$.

12. $2x - 3\sin x + 5 = 0$.

13. $x - \log 10x = 0$.

14. $x \sec x - 1 = 0$.

15. $x \cos x - 1 = 0$.

16. $x^2 - e^x + 2 = 0$.

17. $\sqrt{x} + \sin x - 2 = 0$.

18. $x \log x - 1.2 = 0$.

19. $x^x + 2x - 6 = 0$.

20. $x \tan x - 1.28 = 0$.

21. $x^3 - 10x + 1 = 0$.

22. Find all of the roots both real and imaginary of the equation

$$x^3 - 7x^2 + 5x - 35 = 0$$

Use the Newton-Raphson method.

REFERENCES FOR FURTHER STUDY

JENNINGS, WALTER, *First Course in Numerical Methods*. New York: The Macmillan Company, 1964.

MACON, NATHANIEL, *Numerical Analysis*. New York: John Wiley & Sons, Inc., 1963.

NIELSEN, KAJ J., *Methods in Numerical Analysis*, 2nd ed. New York: The Macmillan Company, 1964.

STANTON, RALPH G., *Numerical Methods for Science and Engineering*. Englewood Cliffs, N.J.: Prentice-Hall, Inc., 1961.

2 COMPLEX ROOTS

2.1 INTRODUCTION

The methods given in chapter 1 are used primarily for finding the real roots of equations. Mechanical systems of many types give rise to linear differential equations with constant coefficients. The solution of such equations may be accomplished in part by the solution of an algebraic equation of degree n where n is the order of the differential equation. When the roots are established they give pertinent information about such things as damping, oscillation, and frequency of oscillation. It is the purpose of this chapter to point out two methods for finding complex roots of such equations.

2.2 COMPLEX ROOTS BY THE NEWTON-RAPHSON METHOD

In the previous chapter we discussed the Newton-Raphson method for the location of real roots of equations. The method also is applicable to equations with complex roots, as shown in the following example.

EXAMPLE. Find the complex roots of the equation

$$x^3 - 2x^2 + 4x - 8 = 0$$

Solution. Here

$$F(x) = x^3 - 2x^2 + 4x - 8$$
$$F'(x) = 3x^2 - 4x + 4$$

and

$$x_{n+1} = x_n - \frac{x_n^3 - 2x_n^2 + 4x_n - 8}{3x_n^2 - 4x_n + 4}$$

Choose a complex starting value such as $x_0 = 1 + i$. Now

$$x_1 = 1 + i - \frac{(1 + i)^3 - 2(1 + i)^2 + 4(1 + i) - 8}{3(1 + i)^2 - 4(1 + i) + 4} = -1 - 2i$$

$$x_2 = (-1 - 2i) - \frac{(-1 - 2i)^3 - 2(-1 - 2i)^2 + 4(-1 - 2i) - 8}{3(-1 - 2i)^2 - 4(-1 - 2i) + 4}$$

$$x_3 = -.937655 - 1.75312i$$

$$x_4 = -.805392 - 1.71677i$$

$$x_5 = -.632212 - 1.71473i$$

$$x_6 = -.425857 - 1.74086i$$

$$x_7 = -.213505 - 1.81222i$$

$$x_8 = -.064789 - 1.91735i$$

$$x_9 = -.014547 - 1.98156i$$

$$x_{10} = -.003504 - 1.99625i$$

$$x_{11} = -.000886 - 1.99910i$$

$$x_{12} = -.000221 - 1.99978i$$

$$x_{13} = -.000055 - 1.99994i$$

$$x_{14} = -.000014 - 1.99999i$$

$$x_{15} = -.000003 - 1.99999i$$

If $x_0 = 0 + 5i$,

$$x_1 = .162102 + 3.47546i$$

$$x_2 = .204739 + 2.57398i$$

$$x_3 = .134266 + 2.14046i$$

$$x_4 = .042421 + 2.02924i$$

$$x_5 = .010761 + 2.00984i$$

$$x_6 = .002728 + 2.00265i$$

$$x_7 = .000685 + 2.00067i$$

$$x_8 = .000172 + 2.00017i$$

$$x_9 = .000043 + 2.00004i$$

$$x_{10} = .000011 + 2.00001i$$

$$x_{11} = .000003 + 2.00000i$$

$$x_{12} = .000000 + 2.00000i$$

Any attempt to calculate real roots with a program to calculate the complex roots is not likely to converge rapidly if at all. If this attempt is made, a starting value $x_0 = a + 0i$ may yield convergence at a very slow rate.

2.3 LIN'S METHOD FOR COMPLEX ROOTS OF ALGEBRAIC EQUATIONS

In order to find the complex roots of an equation of the form

$$a_0x^n + a_1x^{n-1} + a_2x^{n-2} + a_3x^{n-3} + \cdots + a_{n-2}x^2 + a_{n-1}x + a_n = 0 \quad (2.1)$$

we may be able to find real roots, divide out the corresponding factors, and solve the resultant equation. However, if the equation is of even degree there may be no real roots. In such cases we would like to be able to find the quadratic factors of equation (2.1). The following is an iterative procedure for doing this.

Complex roots occur in conjugate pairs, say $(a + bi)$ and $(a - bi)$. The associated factors are

$$x - (a + bi) \quad \text{and} \quad x - (a - bi)$$

From these we construct the quadratic factor

$$[x - (a + bi)][x - (a - bi)] = (x - a - bi)(x - a + bi) \quad (2.2)$$

or

$$[(x - a) - bi][(x - a) + bi] = x^2 - 2ax + a^2 + b^2$$

Now set $x^2 + px + q = x^2 - 2ax + a^2 + b^2$. Equating coefficients,

$$p = -2a$$

$$q = a^2 + b^2$$

and

$$a = \frac{-p}{2}$$

$$b^2 = q - a^2$$

$$b = \pm\sqrt{q - a^2}$$

Now if we can compute p and q, we can find the roots of the factor $x^2 + px + q$. Dividing

$$a_0x^n + a_1x^{n-1} + a_2x^{n-2} + a_3x^{n-3} + \cdots + a_{n-2}x^2 + a_{n-1}x + a_n \quad (2.3)$$

by $x^2 + px + q$, we obtain

$$\frac{a_0x^n + a_1x^{n-1} + a_2x^{n-2} + \cdots + a_{n-2}x^2 + a_{n-1}x + a_n}{x^2 + px + q}$$

$$= b_0x^{n-2} + b_1x^{n-3} + b_2x^{n-4} + \cdots + R$$

where

$$R = b_{n-1}x^{-1} + b_{n-2}x^{-2} \quad (2.4)$$

and

$$b_0 = a_0$$
$$b_1 = a_1 - b_0 p$$
$$b_2 = a_2 - b_0 q - b_1 p$$
$$b_3 = a_3 - b_1 q - b_2 p$$
$$b_4 = a_4 - b_2 q - b_3 p$$

(2.5)

$$b_k = a_k - b_{k-2} q - b_{k-1} p, \qquad k = 2, 3, 4, \ldots, n \qquad (2.6)$$

if $b_{n-1} = b_n = 0$, the remainder term (2.4) would be zero and $x^2 + px + q$ would be a factor. If we stop when we reach the (x^{-1}) term, that is we set $b_n = 0$ and $b_{n-1} = 0$, we have

$$b_{n-1} = a_{n-1} - b_{n-3} q - b_{n-2} p \qquad (2.7)$$

and

$$0 = a_n - b_{n-2} q \qquad (2.8)$$

Solving (2.7) and (2.8) for p and q, we have

$$q = \frac{a_n}{b_{n-2}} \qquad (2.9)$$

$$p = \frac{a_{n-1} - b_{n-3} q}{b_{n-2}} \qquad (2.10)$$

Now we have expressions for p and q which we will use iteratively. As a starting guess for p and q we may use $p = q = 0$. (If that is not possible, use a value nearly zero.)

EXAMPLE.   Solve $x^4 + x^3 + x^2 + x + 1 = 0$, using the iteration:

$$b_1 = a_1 - b_0 p$$

$$b_2 = a_2 - b_0 q - b_1 p$$

$$q = \frac{a_4}{b_2}$$

$$p = \frac{a_3 - b_1 q}{b_2}$$

Solution. We cannot use $p = q = 0$ as this results in $b_2 = 0$ in the first iteration. Instead $p = q = .00001$ was used, and after 400 iterations $p = 1.001579$ and $q = 1.001579$; also then

$$a = \frac{1.001579}{2} = +.5007895$$

$$b = \sqrt{q - a^2} = \sqrt{1.001579 - (+.5007895)^2} = .8664807$$

so that $x = 0.5007895 \pm .8664807i$ where $x = \frac{1}{2} \pm (\sqrt{3}/2)i$ are the correct roots.

For the equation: $7x^4 + 38x^3 + 61x^2 - 30x + 12 = 0$

$$x = .22989091 \pm .3150744i \qquad \text{after seven iterations.}$$

For the equation: $x^4 + 2x^3 + 7x^2 + 8x + 12 = 0$, after 34 iterations,

$$x = -1.0000088 \pm 1.4142418i$$

Note that the approximations to the roots thus determined will be used to construct a quadratic factor $(x^2 + px + q)$ which will be used as a divisor to reduce the degree of the original equation. This new equation will be solved possibly by Lin's method again or, if the reduced equation is of degree two, by the quadratic formula. Any error in the first roots found will cause additional error in successive roots due to the error in the original roots as well as round-off and propagation of the two errors.

PROBLEMS

Find the complex roots of the following equations. Use Lin's method and the Newton-Raphson method.

1. $x^4 + 2x^3 + 7x^2 + 8x + 12 = 0$ [*Ans.* $x = -1 \pm i\sqrt{2}, x = \pm 2i$]

2. $x^4 + x^3 + 32x^2 + 25x + 175 = 0$ [*Ans.* $x = -.5 \pm 2.598i$]

3. $x^4 + 2x^3 + 7x^2 + 8x + 12 = 0$ [*Ans.* $x = \pm 2i, x = -1 \pm i\sqrt{2}$]

4. $x^4 + 8x^3 + 18x^2 + 11x + 2 = 0$

5. $x^4 + 6x^3 + x^2 + 18x + 40 = 0$

6. $x^6 + 7x^5 + 6x^4 + 200x^3 + 80x^2 + 17x + 200 = 0$

7. $x^4 + 8x^3 + 8x^2 + 8x + 7 = 0$

8. $x^6 + 18x^4 + 16x^2 + 18 = 0$

9. $x^3 + 1 = 0$

10. $x^5 + 9x^3 + x^2 - 30x + 5 = 0$

11. $x^6 + x^4 - 5x^2 + 7 = 0$

12. $x^5 + 5x^3 + x^2 + 5 = 0$

REFERENCE

For a noniterative approach see J. B. Scarborough, *Numerical Mathematical Analysis*, 4th ed. (Baltimore: Johns Hopkins Press, 1958), pp. 213–247.

3 SIMULTANEOUS EQUATIONS

3.1 INTRODUCTION

Simultaneous equations are in general much more difficult to solve than are single equations. The iterations are involved and convergence is frequently very slow. Several hundred iterations may be necessary for some sets of this nature. In addition convergence is a much more elusive thing.

3.2 SIMPLE ITERATIVE SOLUTION OF SIMULTANEOUS EQUATIONS

Suppose now that we have two equations in two unknowns that can be expressed in the form

$$x = f_1(x, y)$$

$$y = f_2(x, y)$$

where the functions are continuous and have continuous partial derivatives. Let the first guess be (x_0, y_0) and the first approximation (x_1, y_1) be computed thus:

$$x_1 = f_1(x_0, y_0)$$

$$y_1 = f_2(x_0, y_0)$$

Now

$$x - x_1 = f_1(x, y) - f_1(x_0, y_0)$$

$$y - y_1 = f_2(x, y) - f_2(x_0, y_0)$$

Using the mean value theorem, we may write these equalities

35

$$x - x_1 = (x - x_0)\frac{\overline{\partial f_1}}{\partial x} + (y - y_0)\frac{\overline{\partial f_1}}{\partial y}$$

$$y - y_1 = (x - x_0)\frac{\overline{\partial f_2}}{\partial x} + (y - y_0)\frac{\overline{\partial f_1}}{\partial y}$$

where $\overline{\partial f_1}/\partial x$ is defined to be $\partial f_1/\partial x$ evaluated at

$$[x_0 + \theta(x - x_0),\ y_0 + \theta(y - y_0)] \qquad \text{where } \theta \leq 1.$$

The other partial derivatives are similarly denoted.

Considering absolute values and recognizing that the sum of the absolute values of two terms is equal to or greater than the absolute value of their sum, we can write

$$|x - x_1| \leq |x - x_0|\left|\frac{\overline{\partial f_1}}{\partial x}\right| + |y - y_0|\left|\frac{\overline{\partial f_1}}{\partial y}\right|$$

$$|y - y_1| \leq |x - x_0|\left|\frac{\overline{\partial f_2}}{\partial x}\right| + |y - y_0|\left|\frac{\overline{\partial f_2}}{\partial y}\right|$$

Adding

$$|x - x_1| + |y - y_0| \leq |x - x_0|\left[\left|\frac{\overline{\partial f_1}}{\partial x}\right| + \left|\frac{\overline{\partial f_2}}{\partial x}\right|\right] + |y - y_0|\left[\left|\frac{\overline{\partial f_1}}{\partial y}\right| + \left|\frac{\overline{\partial f_2}}{\partial y}\right|\right]$$

Since the partial derivatives are assumed to exist, the two terms

$$\left[\left|\frac{\overline{\partial f_1}}{\partial x}\right| + \left|\frac{\overline{\partial f_2}}{\partial x}\right|\right] \quad \text{and} \quad \left[\left|\frac{\overline{\partial f_1}}{\partial y}\right| + \left|\frac{\overline{\partial f_2}}{\partial y}\right|\right]$$

must have a maximum value $m > 0$. Then

$$|x - x_1| + |y - y_1| \leq m[|x - x_0| + |y - y_0|]$$
$$|x - x_2| + |y - y_2| \leq m[|x - x_1| + |y - y_1|]$$
$$\cdots\cdots\cdots\cdots\cdots\cdots\cdots\cdots\cdots\cdots\cdots\cdots\cdots\cdots\cdots$$
$$|x - x_n| + |y - y_n| \leq m[|x - x_{n-1}| + |y - y_{n-1}|]$$

Multiplying the inequalities and dividing out the common factors, we get

$$|x - x_n| + |y - y_n| \leq m^n[|x - x_0| + |y - y_0|]$$

Note that $|x - x_n| + |y - y_n|$ will approach zero if $m < 1$.

Sufficient condition for convergence is that $m < 1$. The above inequality does not give any information about convergence if $m \geq 1$; it may converge or it may diverge in such cases. In practice unless m is considerably less than one, convergence is quite slow.

EXAMPLE.   Solve

$$x = y^2 - 3 \log_{10} x$$

$$y = \frac{1}{x} + 2x - 5$$

using $x_0 = 3.4$, $y_0 = 2.2$.

Solution. One gets

$$(x_1, y_1) = (3.25, 1.81)$$

$$(x_2, y_2) = (1.74, .0195)$$

This is apparently diverging.

Since $f_1 = y^2 - 3 \log_{10} x$,

$$\frac{\partial f_1}{\partial y} = 2y, \qquad \frac{\partial f_1}{\partial x} = -\frac{3(.43429)}{x}$$

$$f_2 = \frac{1}{x} + 2x - 5, \qquad \frac{\partial f_2}{\partial y} = 0, \qquad \frac{\partial f_2}{\partial x} = -\frac{1}{x^2} + 2$$

In the neighborhood of the solution $m > 8$. Since this is considerably greater than one, it is not surprising that the process diverges

If the above equations are rearranged to give

$$x = \sqrt{\frac{x(y + 5) - 1}{2}}$$

$$y = \sqrt{x + 3 \log_{10} x}$$

one gets

$$(x_0, y_0) = (3.4, 2.2)$$

$$(x_1, y_1) = (3.426, 2.243)$$

$$(x_2, y_2) = (3.451, 2.2505)$$

$$(x_3, y_3) = (3.466, 2.255)$$

$$(x_4, y_4) = (3.475, 2.258)$$

$$(x_5, y_5) = (3.480, 2.259)$$

$$(x_6, y_6) = (3.483, 2.260)$$

It is left as an exercise for the student to check

$$\left|\frac{\partial \overline{f_1}}{\partial x}\right| + \left|\frac{\partial \overline{f_2}}{\partial x}\right| \qquad \text{and} \qquad \left|\frac{\partial \overline{f_1}}{\partial y}\right| + \left|\frac{\partial \overline{f_2}}{\partial y}\right|$$

for this pair of equations.

3.3 THE NEWTON-RAPHSON METHOD FOR SIMULTANEOUS EQUATIONS

We recall that the Newton-Raphson method may be obtained by writing the function $F(x)$ in a Taylor series expansion about x_0 and truncating after the first derivative. (See Section 1.6.) The Newton-Raphson method for simultaneous equations may be obtained similarly. We will show the approach for two equations.

Let the equations be:

$$F(x, y) = 0$$

$$G(x, y) = 0$$

Denote the first guess as (x_0, y_0). Expand $F(x, y)$ and $G(x, y)$ as Taylor series about (x_0, y_0), truncating each after first derivative terms.

$$F(x, y) = F(x_0, y_0) + \frac{\partial F}{\partial x}\bigg|_0 (x - x_0) + \frac{\partial F}{\partial y}\bigg|_0 (y - y_0) \qquad (3.1a)$$

$$G(x, y) = G(x_0, y_0) + \frac{\partial G}{\partial x}\bigg|_0 (x - x_0) + \frac{\partial G}{\partial y}\bigg|_0 (y - y_0) \qquad (3.1b)$$

where $\dfrac{\partial F}{\partial x}\bigg|_0$ is the value of $\partial F/\partial x$ evaluated at the point (x_0, y_0).

Now let (x_1, y_1) be the first approximation and assume that this point (x_1, y_1) is a good close approximation to the root, so that $F(x_1, y_1)$ is nearly zero as is $G(x_1, y_1)$ also. Substitute (x_1, y_1) into equations (3.1a) and (3.1b) to get

$$F(x_1, y_1) = F(x_0, y_0) + \frac{\partial F}{\partial x}\bigg|_0 (x_1 - x_0) + \frac{\partial F}{\partial y}\bigg|_0 (y_1 - y_0) \qquad (3.1c)$$

$$G(x_1, y_1) = G(x_0, y_0) + \frac{\partial G}{\partial x}\bigg|_0 (x_1 - x_0) + \frac{\partial G}{\partial y}\bigg|_0 (y_1 - y_0) \qquad (3.1d)$$

Since (x_1, y_1) is a good approximation, we set $F(x_1, y_1) = G(x_1, y_1) = 0$ in equations (3.1c) and (3.1d) as follows:

$$F(x_0, y_0) + \frac{\partial F}{\partial x}\bigg|_0 (x_1 - x_0) + \frac{\partial F}{\partial y}\bigg|_0 (y_1 - y_0) = 0 \qquad (3.1e)$$

$$G(x_0, y_0) + \frac{\partial G}{\partial x}\bigg|_0 (x_1 - x_0) + \frac{\partial G}{\partial y}\bigg|_0 (y_1 - y_0) = 0 \qquad (3.1f)$$

Now let

$$x_1 - x_0 = h$$
$$y_1 - y_0 = k \qquad (3.1g)$$

and substitute into (3.1e) and (3.1f). Transposing $F(x_0, y_0)$ and $G(x_0, y_0)$ to the right-hand side of the respective equations,

$$\frac{\partial F}{\partial x}\bigg|_0 h + \frac{\partial F}{\partial y}\bigg|_0 k = -F(x_0, y_0) \qquad (3.1h)$$

$$\frac{\partial G}{\partial x}\bigg|_0 h + \frac{\partial G}{\partial y}\bigg|_0 k = -G(x_0, y_0) \qquad (3.1i)$$

These are linear equations in h and k. A solution may be obtained if

$$\left| \begin{array}{cc} \dfrac{\partial F}{\partial x}\Big|_0 & \dfrac{\partial F}{\partial y}\Big|_0 \\[2mm] \dfrac{\partial G}{\partial x}\Big|_0 & \dfrac{\partial G}{\partial y}\Big|_0 \end{array} \right| \neq 0 \qquad (3.1\mathrm{j})$$

New approximations are

$$x_1 = x_0 + h$$

$$y_1 = y_0 + k$$

Now that a point (x_1, y_1) is obtained, it may be used as point (x_0, y_0) and iterated until convergence to the desired accuracy is obtained. This may require many iterations, if indeed convergence is obtained at all.

EXAMPLE. Solve

$$F(x, y) = x + 3 \log_{10} x - y^2 = 0$$

$$G(x, y) = 2x^2 - xy - 5x + 1 = 0$$

Assuming $x_0 = 2.4$ and $y_0 = 2.2$.

Solution. Here

$$\frac{\partial F}{\partial x} = 1 + \frac{1.30287}{x}, \qquad\qquad \frac{\partial F}{\partial y} = -2y$$

$$\frac{\partial G}{\partial x} = 4x - y - 5, \qquad\qquad \frac{\partial G}{\partial y} = -x$$

$$F(x_0, y_0) = .1545, \qquad\qquad G(x_0, y_0) = -.72$$

$$\frac{\partial F}{\partial x}\bigg|_0 = 1.383, \qquad\qquad \frac{\partial F}{\partial y}\bigg|_0 = -4.4$$

$$\frac{\partial G}{\partial x}\bigg|_0 = 6.4, \qquad\qquad \frac{\partial G}{\partial y}\bigg|_0 = -3.4$$

$$1.383h - 4.4k = -.1545$$

$$6.4h - 3.4k = .72$$

$$h_0 = .157, \qquad k_0 = .085$$

$$x_1 = 3.4 + .157 = 3.557$$

$$y_1 = 2.2 + .085 = 2.285$$

Continuing,

$$(x_2, y_2) = (3.4885, 2.2621)$$

$$(x_3, y_3) = (3.4782, 2.2615)$$

A problem very similar to the above has been programmed for the IBM 1620. The problem is

$$x - y^2 + 3 \log_{10} x = 0$$
$$2x^2 - xy - 5x = 0$$

See Fig. 3.1.

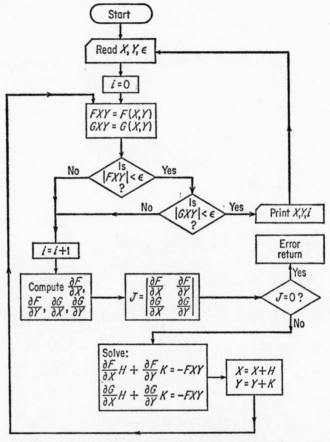

Fig. 3.1 Flow chart for Newton-Raphson solution of two simultaneous equations.

It has been set up so that the iteration will not stop until both the value of h and the value of k are less than 0.00001. The solution is $x = 3.4874422$, $y = 2.2616276$.

The Newton-Raphson method may easily be extended to systems of n equations by simply truncating the Taylor series in exactly the same fashion as with two equations. For example, for three equations

$$F(x, y, z) = 0$$

$$G(x, y, z) = 0$$

$$H(x, y, z) = 0$$

the following equations arise:

$$\frac{\partial F}{\partial x}\bigg|_0 h + \frac{\partial F}{\partial y}\bigg|_0 k + \frac{\partial F}{\partial z}\bigg|_0 l = -F(x_0, y_0, z_0) \qquad (3.1k)$$

$$\frac{\partial G}{\partial x}\bigg|_0 h + \frac{\partial G}{\partial y}\bigg|_0 k + \frac{\partial G}{\partial z}\bigg|_0 l = -G(x_0, y_0, z_0) \qquad (3.1l)$$

$$\frac{\partial H}{\partial x}\bigg|_0 h + \frac{\partial H}{\partial y}\bigg|_0 k + \frac{\partial H}{\partial z}\bigg|_0 l = -H(x_0, y_0, z_0) \qquad (3.1m)$$

where

$$x_1 = x_0 + h$$

$$y_1 = y_0 + k$$

$$z_1 = z_0 + l$$

If the partial derivatives are difficult to calculate, they may be approximated by recalling that

$$\frac{\partial F}{\partial x} = \lim_{\Delta x \to 0} \frac{F(x + \Delta x, y, z) - F(x, y, z)}{\Delta x}$$

We may approximate

$$\frac{\partial F}{\partial x} \quad \text{by} \quad \frac{F(x + \Delta x, y, z) - F(x, y, z)}{\Delta x}$$

or by

$$\frac{F(x + \Delta x, y, z) - F(x - \Delta x, y, z)}{2\Delta x}$$

The other partials can be treated similarly.

3.4 THE METHOD OF STEEPEST DESCENT

Consider the problem of solving the equations:

$$F_1(x, y) = 0 \qquad (3.2)$$

$$F_2(x, y) = 0 \qquad (3.3)$$

Now form the function

$$G(x, y) = [F_1(x, y)]^2 + [F_2(x, y)]^2 \qquad (3.4)$$

$G(x, y)$ is a function having property that any point which is a solution of equations (3.2) and (3.3) is a point which causes $G(x, y)$ to be equal to zero.

Also note that $G(x, y) \geq 0$ for all real x and y. In fact any point which causes $F_1(x, y) = F_2(x, y) = 0$ is a point which is a minimum point of $G(x, y)$. Now our problem is merely to locate the minimum points of $G(x, y)$ and in particular only those minimum points which are absolute minimum points.

If $F_1(x, y)$ and $F_2(x, y)$ are continuous, $G(x, y)$ also will be continuous. The equations $G(x, y) = C$ (a constant) will be closed curves. These closed curves may be considered as contour lines on the surface $z = G(x, y)$, each a distance C above the xy plane.

It is well known that ∇G, the gradient of G, is in the direction of the maximum rate of change of G. Therefore, starting at $p_0(x_0, y_0)$ we should move not in the direction of ∇G, but in the opposite direction given by $-\nabla G$. Now

$$\nabla G = \frac{\partial G}{\partial x}\Big|_0 i + \frac{\partial G}{\partial y}\Big|_0 j$$

and a vector in the appropriate direction

$$\bar{B} = -\nabla G = -\left[\frac{\partial G}{\partial x} i + \frac{\partial G}{\partial y} j \right] \tag{3.5}$$

Now $\hat{B}$ (a unit vector in the direction of $\bar{B}$) is

$$\hat{B} = -\frac{\dfrac{\partial G}{\partial x} i + \dfrac{\partial G}{\partial y} j}{\sqrt{\left(\dfrac{\partial G}{\partial x}\right)^2 + \left(\dfrac{\partial G}{\partial y}\right)^2}} \tag{3.6}$$

Also we have a vector $\bar{A} = (x_1 - x_0)i + (y_1 - y_0)j$, where $p_1(x_1, y_1)$ is a new point on the vector $\bar{B}$. To determine $p_1(x_1, y_1)$ we equate as follows: $\bar{A} = K\hat{B}$ or

$$(x_1 - x_0)i + (y_1 - y_0)j = \frac{+K\left[-\left(\dfrac{\partial G}{\partial x} i + \dfrac{\partial G}{\partial y} j\right) \right]}{\sqrt{\left(\dfrac{\partial G}{\partial x}\right)^2 + \left(\dfrac{\partial G}{\partial y}\right)^2}} \tag{3.7}$$

Since the vectors are equal, their components must also be equal, and we have

$$x_1 - x_0 = \frac{-K\dfrac{\partial G}{\partial x}}{\sqrt{\left(\dfrac{\partial G}{\partial x}\right)^2 + \left(\dfrac{\partial G}{\partial y}\right)^2}} \tag{3.8}$$

$$y_1 - y_0 = \frac{-K\dfrac{\partial G}{\partial y}}{\sqrt{\left(\dfrac{\partial G}{\partial x}\right)^2 + \left(\dfrac{\partial G}{\partial y}\right)^2}} \tag{3.9}$$

or

$$x_1 = x_0 - \frac{K\dfrac{\partial G}{\partial x}}{\sqrt{\left(\dfrac{\partial G}{\partial x}\right)^2 + \left(\dfrac{\partial G}{\partial y}\right)^2}} \qquad (3.10)$$

$$y_1 = y_0 - \frac{K\dfrac{\partial G}{\partial y}}{\sqrt{\left(\dfrac{\partial G}{\partial x}\right)^2 + \left(\dfrac{\partial G}{\partial y}\right)^2}} \qquad (3.11)$$

The procedure is as follows:

Pick a point $p_0(x_0, y_0)$. Use equations (3.10) and (3.11) to compute $p_1(x_1, y_1)$. If $G(x_1, y_1) < G(x_0, y_0)$, there has been an improvement and we continue along the same vector using the same values of the partials previously computed at $p_0(x_0, y_0)$. When a step results in no improvement, that is $G(x_{n+1}, y_{n+1}) \geq G(x_n, y_n)$, divide K by 2, and recompute the partial derivatives at the best previous point. Continuing, we should reach a minimum point. Whether this is a solution of the original equations (3.2) and (3.3) or merely a minimum of $G(x, y)$ is problematical and depends on how good the starting point is and also on the behavior or shape of the function $G(x, y)$.

Variations on the method may involve the frequency with which the partial derivatives are evaluated as the sequence of approximations tends toward a solution or the frequency with which K is changed. One variation is the use of a new K as the square root of the previous K.

The method often results in waste of computer time because a satisfactory starting point has not been found. For some functions, however, any starting point may be satisfactory.

EXAMPLE. Solve

$$x + 2y - 4 = 0$$
$$x - y - 1 = 0$$

using (x_0, y_0) as $(4, 4)$ and $K = 1$.

Solution.

$$G(x, y) = (x + 2y - 4)^2 + (x - y - 1)^2$$

$$\frac{\partial G}{\partial x} = 2(x + 2y - 4) + 2(x - y - 1)$$

$$\frac{\partial G}{\partial y} = 4(x + 2y - 4) - 2(x - y - 1)$$

Evaluating this and substituting into equations (3.10) and (3.11), we have:

X	Y	H
3.6095	3.0794	1.
3.1990	2.1675	1.
2.7478	1.2751	1.
2.1476	.47526	1.
2.2009	.97241	.5
2.0880	.91891	.25
2.0408	1.0347	.125
2.0113	.97959	.0625
2.0104	1.0108	.03125
2.0035	.99680	.015625

These approximations, taking ten iterations for two equations of a very simple type, are indicative of the problems in the use of the method of steepest descent. Starting with $(0, 0)$ and the same routine, convergence was not attained.

3.5 THE WEGSTEIN METHOD FOR TWO FUNCTIONS OF TWO VARIABLES

Consider

$$x = f_1(x, y)$$

$$y = f_2(x, y)$$

There are several ways in which these might be solved using an iterative technique. The procedure that we will describe here has been programmed for the IBM 704 at the General Motors Research Laboratories and has been highly successful in the past.

Let us first review the Wegstein method for functions of one variable. The order of computation is as follows:

$$x_1 = f(x_0)$$

$$x_2 = f(x_1)$$

$$a = \frac{f(x_1) - f(x_0)}{x_1 - x_0} = \frac{x_2 - x_0}{x_1 - x_0}$$

$$q = \frac{a}{a - 1}$$

$$\bar{x}_2 = qx_1 + (1 - q)x_2$$

$$x_3 = f(\bar{x}_2)$$

$$a = \frac{f(\bar{x}_2) - f(x_1)}{\bar{x}_2 - x_1}$$

$$q = \frac{a}{a-1}$$

$$\bar{x}_3 = q\bar{x}_2 + (1-q)x_3$$

$$x_4 = f(\bar{x}_3)$$

$$a = \frac{x_4 - x_3}{\bar{x}_4 - \bar{x}_3}$$

$$q = \frac{a}{a-1}$$

For two functions of two variables

$$x = f_1(x, y)$$

$$y = f_2(x, y)$$

with a starting guess (x_0, y_0):

(1) Solve $x = f_1(x_0, y_0)$ holding y_0 constant. Call the solution x_1^*. This solution is the value that $\bar{x}_k$ converges to with y_0 fixed. There are a good many calculations involved in just this one operation.

(2) Compute $y_1 = f_2(x_1^*, y_0)$.

(3) Solve $x = f_1(x, y_1)$. Call the solution x_2^*.

(4) Compute $y_2 = f(x_2^*, y_1)$.

(5) Use the Wegstein interpolation on the y's to obtain $\bar{y}_2$.

(6) Solve $x = f_1(x, \bar{y}_2)$ for x_3^*.

(7) Obtain y_3 and $\bar{y}_3$.

(8) Continue the process, interpolating for $\bar{y}_k$ after obtaining x_k^*. The $\bar{y}_k$'s converge to the required value of y and the x_k^* converge to the required x. The process is stopped when $\bar{y}_{k+1}$ is sufficiently close to $\bar{y}_k$.

3.6 THE WEGSTEIN METHOD FOR THREE EQUATIONS IN THREE UNKNOWNS

This method has been programmed as a subroutine for the IBM 704 at the General Motors Research Laboratories.

For the equations

$$x = f_1(x, y, z)$$

$$y = f_2(x, y, z)$$

$$z = f_3(x, y, z)$$

with a starting guess (x_0, y_0, z_0):

(1) The single equation $x = f_1(x, y_0, z_0)$ is solved as in the previous section, giving a solution x_1^*.

(2) Compute $y_1 = f_2(x_1^*, y_0, z_0)$.

(3) $x = f_1(x, y_1, z_0)$ is solved for x_2^*.

(4) Compute $y_2 = f_2(x_2^*, y_1, z_0)$.

(5) Use the Wegstein interpolation on y_0, y_1, and y_2 to obtain $\bar{y}_2$.

(6) Solve $x = f_1(x, \bar{y}_2, z_0)$ for x_3^*.

(7) $y_3 = f_2(x_3^*, \bar{y}_2, z_0)$. Now find $\bar{y}_3$, using the last y's.

(8) Continue in this way until we obtain a $\bar{y}_{n+1}$ sufficiently close to $\bar{y}_n$. When this occurs, we have solutions x_{n+1}^*, $\bar{y}_{n+1}$ that satisfy the first two equations when $z = z_0$.

(9) $z_1 = f_3(x_{n+1}^*, \bar{y}_{n+1}, z_0)$.

(10) Repeat steps 1 through 8 with $z = z_1$. Then use the last equation and the "best" values of x and y to find z_2.

(11) Having z_0, z_1, and z_2, use the Wegstein interpolation to find $\bar{z}_2$.

(12) Repeat steps 1 through 11 until $\bar{z}_{k+1}$ is sufficiently close to $\bar{z}_k$. The last values obtained should satisfy all three equations to within agreed tolerances.

It is apparent that the application of this method to the solution of more than two equations in two unknowns is not justified if one has only a desk calculator. Indeed, the determination of only five x^*'s in the problem of Section 3.5 is approximately a three-hour job on a desk calculator.

PROBLEMS

1. Solve by the method of simple iteration. Check the appropriate partial derivatives.

$$y - \sin x + 1.32 = 0$$
$$x - \cos y - 0.85 = 0$$

2. Solve by the method of Newton-Raphson:

$$x = y^2 - 3 \log_{10} x$$
$$y = \frac{1}{x} + 2x - 5.$$

Use a starting guess (3.4, 2.2).

3. Solve problem 2 by the Wegstein method.

4. Solve problem 1 by the method of Newton-Raphson.

5. Solve by an iterative method:

$$x + \tan y = 0$$
$$e^x - y - 2 = 0$$

[*Solutions:* $x = .88304$, $y = 2.4182$, $x = -.60656$, $y = .54523$]

6. Solve by an iterative method:

$$x - y^2 + 3 \log_{10} x = 0$$
$$2x^2 - xy - 5x = 0$$

[*Solutions:* $x = 3.4874$, $y = 2.2616$]

7. Solve by an iterative method:

$$4x^3 - 27xy^2 + 25 = 0$$
$$4x^2y - 3y^3 - 1 = 0$$

4 INTERPOLATION TECHNIQUES

4.1 INTRODUCTION

Interpolation is the process of finding the value of a function at some arbitrary point when the function is not known and is represented in a given range as a table of discrete points, as in Table 4.1. Interpolation is necessary

Table 4.1

x	y
0	4
1	5
2	7
3	9
4	16
5	27
6	32

to find y when x is some value not given in the table. For instance, find y when $x = 2.7$. The process of finding x when y is known may be referred to as inverse interpolation. For our purposes the independent variable will be tabulated at even intervals, so that for all defined values of x:

$$x_{i+1} - x_i = h \quad \text{(where } h \text{ is a constant)}$$

4.2 FORWARD DIFFERENCES

Consider a table such as Table 4.1. Now we can define forward differences as:

$$\Delta y_i = y_{i+1} - y_i$$

48

Again if we difference the forward difference, we obtain

$$\Delta^2 y_i = \Delta(\Delta y_i) = \Delta(y_{i+1} - y_i) = y_{i+2} - 2y_{i+1} + y_i$$

and

$$\Delta^3 y_i = \Delta(\Delta^2 y_i) = \Delta(y_{i+2} - 2y_{i+1} + y_i) = y_{i+3} - 3y_{i+2} + 3y_{i+1} - y_i$$

and

$$\Delta^4 y_i = y_{i+4} - 4y_{i+3} + 6y_{i+2} - 4y_{i+1} + y_i$$

Now the coefficients appear to take on a pattern. They are the binomial coefficients. These coefficients may be written as

$$\binom{n}{k} = \frac{n(n-1)(n-2) \cdots (n-k+1)}{k!}$$

where k is a positive integer. Additional relationships involving the binomial coefficients are

$$\binom{n}{k} = \binom{n}{n-k} \quad \text{and} \quad \binom{n+1}{k} = \binom{n}{k} + \binom{n}{k-1}$$

With the aid of the binomial coefficients, we can write the nth difference as

$$\Delta^n y_0 = \sum_{i=0}^{n} (-1)^i \binom{n}{i} y_{n-i}$$

Similarly, we can express y in terms of an initial value and its differences:

$$y_i = y_{i-1} + (y_i - y_{i-1}) = y_{i-1} + \Delta y_{i-1}$$

thus

$$y_1 = y_0 + \Delta y_0$$

For higher differences

$$\Delta^n y_i = \Delta^{n+1} y_{i-1} + \Delta^n y_{i-1}$$

For example,

$$\Delta^3 y_0 = y_3 - 3y_2 + 3y_1 - y_0$$

or

$$y_3 = 3(y_2 - y_1) + y_0 + \Delta^3 y_0 = \Delta^3 y_0 + 3\Delta y_1 + y_0$$

but

$$\Delta y_1 = \Delta y_0 + \Delta^2 y_0$$

so that

$$y_3 = \Delta^3 y_0 + 3(\Delta y_0 + \Delta^2 y_0) + y_0$$

or

$$y_3 = \Delta^3 y_0 + 3\,\Delta^2 y_0 + 3\,\Delta y_0 + y_0$$

This brings to mind the binomial coefficients again. Without proof we write

$$y_k = y_0 + \binom{k}{1} \Delta y_0 + \binom{k}{2} \Delta^2 y_0 + \cdots + \Delta^k y_0$$

or, more compactly,

$$y_k = \sum_{i=0}^{k} \binom{k}{i} \Delta^i y_0$$

4.3 ERRORS IN TABLES

For purposes of hand calculation differences may be arranged as shown in Table 4.2.

Table 4.2

x	y	Δy	$\Delta^2 y$	$\Delta^3 y$	$\Delta^4 y$
x_0	y_0				
		Δy_0			
x_1	y_1		$\Delta^2 y_0$		
		Δy_1		$\Delta^3 y_0$	
x_2	y_2		$\Delta^2 y_1$		$\Delta^4 y_0$
		Δy_2		$\Delta^3 y_1$	
x_3	y_3		$\Delta^2 y_2$		$\Delta^4 y_1$
		Δy_3		$\Delta^3 y_2$	
x_4	y_4		$\Delta^2 y_3$		$\Delta^4 y_2$
		Δy_4		$\Delta^3 y_3$	
x_5	y_5		$\Delta^2 y_4$		
		Δy_5			
x_6	y_6				

Let us examine a table of x versus y where there is an error, ε, in one of the tabular values of y. A careful examination of Table 4.3 shows that

Table 4.3

x	y	Δy	$\Delta^2 y$	$\Delta^3 y$	$\Delta^4 y$
x_{-3}	y_{-3}				
		Δy_{-3}			
x_{-2}	y_{-2}		$\Delta^2 y_{-3}$		$\Delta^4 y_{-4} + \varepsilon$
		Δy_{-2}		$\Delta^3 y_{-3} + \varepsilon$	
x_{-1}	y_{-1}		$\Delta^2 y_{-2} + \varepsilon$		$\Delta^4 y_{-3} - 4\varepsilon$
		$\Delta y_{-1} + \varepsilon$		$\Delta^3 y_{-2} - 3\varepsilon$	
x_0	$y_0 + \varepsilon$		$\Delta^2 y_{-1} - 2\varepsilon$		$\Delta^4 y_{-2} + 6\varepsilon$
		$\Delta y_0 - \varepsilon$		$\Delta^3 y_{-1} + 3\varepsilon$	
x_1	y_1		$\Delta^2 y_0 + \varepsilon$		$\Delta^4 y_{-1} - 4\varepsilon$
		Δy_1		$\Delta^3 y_0 - \varepsilon$	
x_2	y_2		$\Delta^2 y_1$		$\Delta^4 y_0 + \varepsilon$
		Δy_2			
x_3	y_3				

the error, ε, in y_0 spreads in a triangular form throughout the table. This spreading of the errors through the table will cause errors in interpolated values even where the correct y values are given. This results because higher-order differences are used in calculating the interpolated y value. Thus we must be very careful with our input data if we wish to achieve good interpolated results. Often we cannot do any better than a linear interpolation because the data are derived by experiment and subject to statistical error, recording error, and in some cases noise.

The following characteristics of error growth in a difference table can be observed:

(1) The coefficients of ε's are the binomial coefficients with alternating signs.

(2) The algebraic sum of the errors in any difference column is zero.

(3) The maximum error in the even differences is in the same horizontal line as the tabular value in error (y_0 in the above example).

Table 4.4 gives a numerical example of a diagonal difference table. Note that in accordance with the usual practice the decimal points and leading zeros have been omitted in entering the differences.

Table 4.4

x	y	Δy	$\Delta^2 y$	$\Delta^3 y$	$\Delta^4 y$
1.0	1.0000				
		5191			
1.1	1.5191		354		
		5545		−24	
1.2	2.0736		330		24
		5875		0	
1.3	2.6611		330		24
		6205		24	
1.4	3.2816		354		51
		6559		75	
1.5	3.9375		429		−84
		6988		−9	
1.6	4.6363		420		186
		7408		177	
1.7	5.3771		597		−84
		8005		93	
1.8	6.1776		690		51
		8695		144	
1.9	7.0471		834		
		9529			
2.0	8.0000				

Consider Table 4.4, and assume that the fourth differences should be constant or approximately so. Note that the fourth differences are oscillating for the higher values of x with the largest absolute value of 186. This suggests that the y value for $x = 1.6$ is in error. From Table 4.3 we can write

$$\Delta^4 y_{-4} + \varepsilon = 51$$

$$\Delta^4 y_{-3} - 4\varepsilon = -84$$

$$\Delta^4 y_{-2} + 6\varepsilon = 186$$

$$\Delta^4 y_{-1} - 4\varepsilon = -84$$

$$\Delta^4 y_0 + \varepsilon = 51$$

We can eliminate $\Delta^4 y$ from any two of the above equations and solve for ε. Subtracting the second from the first, we get

$$5\varepsilon = 135$$

$$\varepsilon = 27$$

Then $y(1.6) + \varepsilon = 4.6363$, and the correct y is 4.6336.

The error in this case was caused by the transposition of two digits, which is a common error in transcribing data. A transposition of two adjacent digits which differ by m will produce an error ε of $9m$ in their digit positions.

4.4 LINEAR INTERPOLATION

Given a table such as Table 4.2, we wish to interpolate for y when x is given in the table. Perhaps x is between x_0 and x_1; if not, the table can be rewritten so that it is. Now we can draw a picture (Fig. 4.1) and write the equation of the straight line through the points (x_0, y_0) and (x_1, y_1).

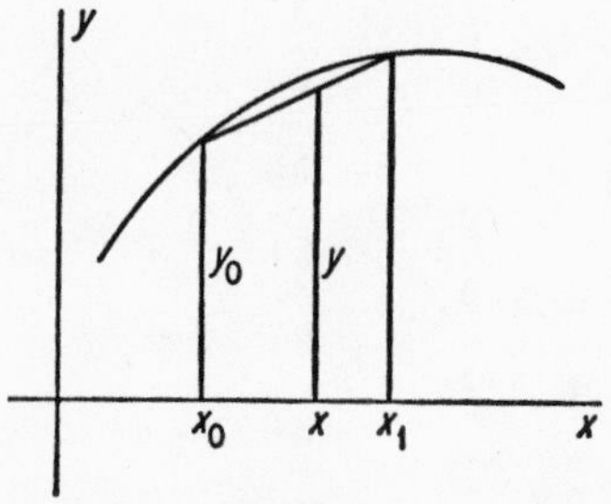

$$y - y_0 = \frac{y_1 - y_0}{x_1 - x_0}(x - x_0) \qquad (4.1)$$

Equation (4.1) can be solved for y as

$$y = y_0 + \frac{(y_1 - y_0)(x - x_0)}{x_1 - x_0}$$

or

$$y = \frac{y_0(x - x_0) + (y_1 - y_0)(x - x_0)}{x_1 - x_0}$$

Fig. 4.1.

and upon simplification

$$y = \frac{y_0(x_1 - x) - y_1(x_0 - x)}{x_1 - x_0} \qquad (4.2)$$

Equation (4.2) can be written with the aid of an obvious determinant as

$$y = \frac{1}{x_1 - x_0} \begin{vmatrix} y_0 & (x_0 - x) \\ y_1 & (x_1 - x) \end{vmatrix} \qquad (4.3)$$

Equation (4.3) can, of course, also be expressed as

$$y = y_0 + \frac{(x - x_0) \Delta y}{\Delta x}$$

where $\Delta y = y_1 - y_0$ and $\Delta x = x_1 - x_0$, as most of us have done in high school trigonometry.

For example, find y at $x = .3421$.

i	x_i	y_i	$x_i - x$
0	.3412	.1946	−.0009
1	.3432	.1273	.0011

$$y(.3421) = \frac{1}{.0020} [(.1946)(.0011) - (.1273)(-.0009)]$$

$$= .1643$$

4.5 DIFFERENCES AND POLYNOMIALS

It can be shown by mathematical induction that for nth degree polynomials the nth differences are constant and the $(n + 1)$st differences are zero. The converse is also valid and useful in interpolation. That is, if k differences are zero, the function represented is a polynomial of degree $k - 1$.

Newton's forward difference formula. Let us consider y as a function of x which takes on the values $y = y_0, y_1, y_2, y_3, \ldots, y_n$ for $x = x_0, x_1, x_2, x_3$ where $x_{i+1} - x_i = h$. Let $P_n(x)$ be a polynomial in x of degree n as follows:

$$P_n(x) = a_0 + a_1(x - x_0) + a_2(x - x_0)(x - x_1) + a_3(x - x_0)(x - x_1)(x - x_2)$$

$$+ \cdots + a_n(x - x_0)(x - x_1)(x - x_2) \cdots (x - x_{n-2})(x - x_{n-1})$$

$$(4.4)$$

Now we can determine the coefficients a_i such that

$$P_n(x_0) = y_0$$

$$P_n(x_1) = y_1$$

$$\cdot$$

$$\cdot$$

$$P_n(x_n) = y_n$$

Since $x_{i+1} - x_i = h$, we may write

$$x_{i+1} = x_i + h$$

and, letting $i = 0$, we have

$$x_1 = x_0 + h$$
$$x_2 = x_1 + h = x_0 + h + h = x_0 + 2h$$
$$x_3 = x_2 + h = x_0 + 2h + h = x_0 + 3h$$

or, in general,

$$x_i = x_0 + ih \quad \text{or} \quad x_i - x_0 = ih \quad \text{for } i = 1, 2, 3, \ldots, n$$

Let x assume the values of $x_0, x_1, x_2, \ldots, x_n$ in equation (4.4) and set $P_n(x_i) = y_i$. Now we have

$$P_n(x_0) = y_0 = a_0$$
$$P_n(x_1) = y_1 = a_0 + a_1(x_1 - x_0) = a_0 + a_1 h$$
$$P_n(x_2) = y_2 = a_0 + a_1(x_2 - x_0) + a_2(x_2 - x_0)(x_2 - x_1)$$
$$= a_0 + a_1(2h) + a_2(2h)(h) \qquad (4.5)$$

$$\vdots$$

$$P_n(x_i) = y_i = a_0 + a_1(ih) + a_2(ih)[(i - 1)h] + a_n n! h^i$$

Solving equations (4.5) for the a_i, we have

$$a_0 = y_0$$

$$a_1 = \frac{y_1 - a_0}{h} = \frac{y_1 - y_0}{h} = \frac{\Delta y_0}{h}$$

$$a_2 = \frac{1}{2h^2}\left[y_2 - a_0 - 2ha_1\right] = \frac{1}{2h^2}\left[y_2 - y_0 - 2h\right]\frac{y_1 - y_0}{h} = \frac{1}{2h^2}\left[\Delta^2 y_0\right]$$

or, in general,

$$a_n = \frac{\Delta^n y_0}{n! h^n}$$

Substituting these values of a_n into equation (4.4), we obtain

$$P_n(x) = y_0 + \frac{\Delta y_0}{h}(x - x_0) + \frac{\Delta^2 y_0}{2! h^2}(x - x_0)(x - x_1) + \cdots$$

$$+ \frac{\Delta^n y_0}{n! h^n}(x - x_0)(x - x_1) \cdots (x - x_{n-1}) \qquad (4.6)$$

Equation (4.6) is the Newton forward interpolation formula written in terms of x. It is also referred to as the Newton-Gregory formula, since a recently discovered letter indicates it was derived by Gregory around 1670.

We can simplify equation (4.6) with a transformation on the variable of the form

$$u = \frac{x - x_0}{h} \quad \text{or} \quad x = x_0 + hu$$

Since $x_1 = x_0 + h$ and $x_2 = x_0 + 2h$, etc., we have

$$x_i = x_0 + ih$$

and

$$\frac{x - x_i}{h} = \frac{x - (x_0 + ih)}{h} = \frac{x - x_0}{h} - i = u - i$$

Now we substitute

$$\frac{x - x_i}{h} = u - i$$

into equation (4.6).

$$y = P_n(x) = P_n(x_0 + hu) = y_0 + \frac{u \, \Delta y_0}{1!} + \frac{u(u - 1)}{2!} \Delta^2 y_0 + \cdots$$

$$+ \frac{u(u - 1)(u - 2) \cdots (u - n + 1)}{n!} \Delta^n y_0 \qquad (4.7)$$

This is the usual form for the Newton forward formula.

EXAMPLE. Given the table of x versus y as follows:

x	2	4	6	8	10	12	14
y	23	93	259	569	1071	1873	2843

We construct a forward difference table (Table 4.5). Let us find y when

Table 4.5

x	y	Δy	$\Delta^2 y$	$\Delta^3 y$
2	23			
		70		
4	93		96	
		166		48
6	259		144	
		310		48
8	569		192	
		502		48
10	1071		240	
		742		48
12	1813		288	
		1030		
14	2843			

$x = 4.2$. We may pick x_0 anyplace in the table, so we pick $x_0 = 4$. Now the differences necessary for hand calculation of y fall on a diagonal line down from x_0 as shown. (Of course $h = 2$.) Now

$$u = \frac{4.2 - 4}{2} = \frac{.2}{2} = .1$$

Substituting into equation (4.7), we have

$$y = 93 + \frac{.1(166)}{1!} + \frac{.1(.1 - 1)(144)}{2!} + \frac{.1(.1 - 1)(.1 - 2)(48)}{3!}$$

$$y = 104.488$$

Since Table 4.5 has constant third differences, we may conclude that it is derived from a cubic polynomial

$$y = x^3 + 7x + 1$$

If we substitute $x = 4.2$ into the above cubic, we get $y = 104.488$.

The construction of a table of forward differences permits us to see that interpolation to a high degree toward the bottom of the table with Newton's forward formula will not be as accurate, since the higher differences disappear.

In digital computer interpolation it is necessary to store only the table of x and y. From this we can compute the necessary differences with simple expressions for the various differences. This saves much time and space over storing the differences also.

4.6 THE OPERATORS E AND Δ

Let us define the shifting operator E which transforms a function as follows:

$$Ef(x_n) = f(x_n + h) \quad \text{or} \quad Ey_n = y_{n+1}$$

Also

$$E^2f(x_n) = E[Ef(x)] = E[f(x_n + h)] = f(x_n + 2h)$$

or, in general,

$$E^uf(x_n) = f(x_n + uh)$$

The identity operator $E^0f(x_n) = f(x_n)$ leaves $f(x_n)$ unchanged. The forward difference $\Delta f(x_n) = f(x_n + h) - f(x_n)$ may be written as:

$$f(x_n + h) = f(x_n) + \Delta f(x_n)$$

Now, noticing the shifting operator again,

$$Ef(x_n) = f(x_n) + \Delta f(x_n)$$
$$Ef(x_n) = (1 + \Delta)f(x_n)$$

where we are also regarding differencing as an operator. Symbolically, then,

$$E = 1 + \Delta.$$

Now

$$P_n(x_0 + hu) = E^u P_n(x_0) = E^u y_0 = (1 + \Delta)^u y_0 \qquad (4.8)$$

Expanding formally the right side of equation (4.8) by the binomial theorem, we obtain

$$y = P_n(x_0 + hu)$$

$$= \left[1 + \binom{u}{1} \Delta y_0 + \binom{u}{2} \Delta^2 y_0 + \cdots + \binom{u}{i} \Delta^i + \cdots + \binom{u}{n} \Delta^n \right] y_0$$

or

$$y = P_n(x_0 + hu)$$

$$= y_0 + u \,\Delta y_0 + \binom{u}{2} \Delta^2 y_0 + \cdots + \binom{u}{i} \Delta^i y_0 + \cdots + \binom{u}{n} \Delta^n y_0$$

We can reduce the bulk of this expression by summing as

$$y = P_n(x_0 + hu) = y_0 + \sum_{i=1}^{n} \binom{u}{i} \Delta^i y_0 \qquad (4.9)$$

The operator technique is a very quick way to useful results in many situations.

4.7 NEWTON'S BACKWARD INTERPOLATION FORMULA

To obtain a formula useful for calculating values toward the end of a table, we define another operator ∇ (the backward difference operator) which transforms the function $f(x)$ as follows:

$$\nabla f(x_n) = f(x_n) - f(x_{n-1}) \qquad (4.10)$$

or

$$\nabla y_n = y_n - y_{n-1}; \qquad x_{i+1} - x_i = h \quad \text{(a constant)} \qquad (4.11)$$

Continuing to second differences:

$$\nabla^2 y_n = \nabla(\nabla y_n) = \nabla(y_n - y_{n-1}) = \nabla y_n - \nabla y_{n-1}$$

$$\nabla^2 y_n = y_n - y_{n-1} - (y_{n-1} - y_{n-2}) = y_n - 2y_{n-1} + y_{n-2}$$

In a similar manner:

$$\nabla^3 y_n = \nabla(\nabla^2 y_n) = \nabla(y_n - 2y_{n-1} + y_{n-2})$$

$$\nabla^3 y_n = \nabla y_n - 2\,\nabla y_{n-1} + \nabla y_{n-2}$$

$$\nabla^3 y_n = y_n - y_{n-1} - 2(y_{n-1} - y_{n-2}) + y_{n-2} - y_{n-3}$$

$$\nabla^3 y_n = y_n - 3y_{n-1} + 3y_{n-2} - y_{n-3}$$

Higher differences may be obtained in a similar fashion. Note the appearance of binomial coefficients and the sign alternations. Also note that forward differences may be expressed as backward differences; that is,

$$\Delta y_n = y_{n+1} - y_n = \nabla y_{n+1} \quad \text{and so on.}$$

Now we develop an interpolating polynomial beginning at (x_n, y_n) where x_n is the end point rather than the initial point. (Of course any point may be regarded as the end point.) Let

$$P_n(x) = a_0 + a_1(x - x_n) + a_2(x - x_n)(x - x_{n-1})$$
$$+ a_3(x - x_n)(x - x_{n-1})(x - x_{n-2}) + \cdots$$
$$+ a_n(x - x_n)(x - x_{n-1})(x - x_{n-2}) \cdots (x - x_1)$$

Also let $P_n(x)$ assume the value y_n when $x = x_n$. Now

$$P_n(x_n) = y_n = a_0$$
$$P_n(x_{n-1}) = y_{n-1} = a_0 + a_1(x_{n-1} - x_n) = a_0 + a_1 h$$
$$P_n(x_{n-2}) = y_{n-2} = a_0 + a_1(x_{n-2} - x_n) + a_2(x_{n-2} - x_n)(x_{n-2} - x_{n-1})$$
$$= a_0 + 2ha_1 + a_2(2h)(h)$$

$$\vdots \qquad\qquad \vdots$$

Solve for the a_i:

$$a_0 = y_n$$

$$a_1 = \frac{y_{n-1} - a_0}{-h} = \frac{y_n - y_{n-1}}{h}$$

$$a_2 = \frac{y_{n-2} - a_0 + 2ha_1}{2h^2} = \frac{(y_{n-2} - y_n) + 2(y_n - y_{n-1})}{2h^2}$$

$$= \frac{y_{n-2} - 2y_{n-1} + y_n}{2h^2} = \frac{y_n - 2y_{n-1} + y_{n-2}}{2h^2} = \frac{\nabla^2 y_n}{2h^2}$$

In general, $a_n = \nabla^n y_n / n! h^n$ and

$$P_n(x) = y_n + \frac{\nabla y_n}{h}(x - x_n) + \frac{\nabla^2 y_n}{2! h^2}(x - x_n)(x - x_{n-1})$$

$$+ \frac{\nabla^3 y_n}{3! h^3}(x - x_n)(x - x_{n-1})(x - x_{n-2}) + \cdots$$

$$+ \frac{\nabla^n y_n}{n! h^n}(x - x_n)(x - x_{n-1}) \cdots (x - x_1)$$

We may transform the variable by letting

$$u = \frac{x - x_n}{h} \tag{4.12}$$

$x = x_n + hu$, so that

$$\frac{x - x_i}{h} = \frac{x - (x_n - ih)}{h} = \frac{x - x_n}{h} + \frac{ih}{h} = u + i$$

Now

$$P_n(x) = P_n(x + hu) = y_n + u\nabla y_n + \frac{u(u + 1)}{2!}\nabla^2 y_n$$

$$+ \frac{u(u + 1)(u + 2)}{3!}\nabla^3 y_n + \cdots \quad (4.13)$$

This is Newton's backward interpolation formula.

Another approach is in terms of the operator E and the operator ∇. Formally we write

$$\nabla = 1 - E^{-1} \quad (4.14)$$

This appears reasonable, since when we operate on y_n with both sides of (4.14) we obtain the same result:

$$(1 - E^{-1})y_n = y_n - E^{-1}y_n = y_n - y_{n-1} = \nabla y_n$$

or

$$\nabla y_n = (1 - E^{-1})y_n \quad (4.15)$$

Again we obtain formally from (4.15)

$$1 - E^{-1} = \nabla$$

$$E^{-1} = 1 - \nabla$$

$$E = (1 - \nabla)^{-1} \quad (4.16)$$

Now

$$E^u P_n(x_n) = P_n(x_n + hu) = (1 - \nabla)^{-u}y_n \quad (4.17)$$

or, by the binomial theorem on equation (4.17),

$$y = P_n(x_n + hu) = \left[1 + (-u)(1)(-\nabla) + \frac{(-u)(-u - 1)}{2!}(-\nabla^2) + \cdots\right]y_n$$

$$y = \left[1 + u\nabla + \frac{u(u + 1)}{2!}\nabla^2 + \cdots\right]y_n$$

$$y = y_n + u\nabla y_n + \frac{u(u + 1)}{2!}\nabla^2 y_n + \frac{u(u + 1)(u + 2)}{3!}\nabla^3 y_n$$

$$+ \frac{u(u + 1)(u + 2)(u + 3)}{4!}\nabla^4 y_n + \cdots \quad (4.18)$$

Again Newton's backward formula.

EXAMPLE. Find y when $x = 11.8$ for the data in Table 4.6.

Table 4.6

x	y			
2	23			
		70		
4	93		96	
		166		48
6	259		144	
		310		48
8	569		192	
		502		48
10	1071		240	
		742		48
12	1813		288	
		1030		
14	2843			

Solution. Pick $x_n = 12$. Now the appropriate differences lie on the diagonal line upward to the right. By equation (4.12)

$$u = \frac{11.8 - 12}{2} = -.1$$

Now, by equation (4.13),

$$y = 1813 + (-.1)(742) + \frac{(-.1)(-.1 + 1)(240)}{1 \cdot 2}$$

$$+ \frac{(-.1)(-.1 + 1)(-.1 + 2)(48)}{1 \cdot 2 \cdot 3}$$

or

$$y = 1726.632$$

4.8 AITKEN'S REPEATED PROCESS

One of the more practical and simple methods for machine computation of the various interpolation schemes is Aitken's repeated process. It is merely a repeated application of linear interpolation. As was shown previously, a linear interpolation can be written as

$$y(x) = \frac{1}{x_1 - x_0} \begin{vmatrix} y_0 & (x_0 - x) \\ y_1 & (x_1 - x) \end{vmatrix}$$

This interpolates in the interval $x_0 \leq x \leq x_1$. We may also write

$$y(x) = \frac{1}{x_2 - x_0} \begin{vmatrix} y_0 & (x_0 - x) \\ y_2 & (x_2 - x) \end{vmatrix}$$

If the function we are interpolating is a straight line, we get the same value for $y(x)$ as before.

We will use the following notation:

$$y_{11}(x) = y(x), \qquad x_0 \le x \le x_1$$

$$y_{21}(x) = y(x), \qquad x_0 \le x \le x_2$$

$$y_{i1}(x) = y(x), \qquad x_0 \le x \le x_i$$

Now we have

$$y_{i1} = \frac{1}{x_i - x_0} \begin{vmatrix} y_0 & (x_0 - x) \\ y_i & (x_i - x) \end{vmatrix} \qquad (4.19)$$

We can now build up a table

$$
\begin{array}{ll}
x_0 & \\
x_1 & y_{11}(x) \\
x_2 & y_{21}(x) \\
x_3 & y_{31}(x) \\
x_4 & y_{41}(x) \\
\cdot & \\
\cdot & \\
\cdot & \\
\end{array}
$$

From this table we can again apply linear interpolation,

$$y_{22}(x) = \frac{1}{x_2 - x_1} \begin{vmatrix} y_{11}(x) & (x_1 - x) \\ y_{21}(x) & (x_2 - x) \end{vmatrix}$$

or, in general,

$$y_{i2}(x) = \frac{1}{x_i - x_1} \begin{vmatrix} y_{11}(x) & (x_1 - x) \\ y_{i1}(x) & (x_i - x) \end{vmatrix} \qquad (4.20)$$

Now we can build a new table (Table 4.7). By substitution into equation

Table 4.7

$$
\begin{array}{ll}
x_2 & y_{22}(x) \\
x_3 & y_{32}(x) \\
x_4 & y_{42}(x) \\
\cdot & \cdot \\
\cdot & \cdot \\
\cdot & \cdot \\
x_i & y_{i2}(x) \\
\end{array}
$$

(4.20) it can be shown that equation (4.20) is a polynomial of degree two which passes through the points (x_0, y_0), (x_2, y_2), and (x_1, y_1). If we interpolate with this process, we get from y_{i2} an interpolation of degree two. The procedure can be extended to degree three by interpolating in Table 4.7. In fact, interpolation of any desired degree can be achieved by extending these tables. Higher than third-order interpolation usually is not attempted. The method is limited because of error propagation, and the high-order polynomials may not be sufficiently accurate. An important consideration is that the use of the Aitken's repeated process is *not* limited to uniformly spaced data.

EXAMPLE. Find y at $x = 2.5$ from the tabular data:

n	x	y	y_{i2}
0	1	1	
1	3	9	7
2	4	16	8.5
3	6	36	11.5

Solution.

$$y_{11} = \frac{1}{3-1} \begin{vmatrix} 1 & (1-2.5) \\ 9 & (3-2.5) \end{vmatrix} = 7$$

$$y_{21} = \frac{1}{4-1} \begin{vmatrix} 1 & (1-2.5) \\ 16 & (4-2.5) \end{vmatrix} = 8.5$$

$$y_{31} = \frac{1}{6-1} \begin{vmatrix} 1 & (1-2.5) \\ 36 & (6-2.5) \end{vmatrix} = 11.5$$

Now

$$y_{22} = \frac{1}{4-3} \begin{vmatrix} 7 & (3-2.5) \\ 8.5 & (4-2.5) \end{vmatrix} = 6.25$$

$$y_{32} = \frac{1}{6-3} \begin{vmatrix} 7 & (3-2.5) \\ 11.5 & (6-2.5) \end{vmatrix} = 6.25$$

Note the y_{22} and y_{32} are equal. The reason is that the table is actually a table of squares, i.e., a polynomial of degree two which y_{i2} fits exactly.

4.9 INVERSE INTERPOLATION

Inverse interpolation is the process of finding the value of the argument x corresponding to a given function y which is between two tabulated values. One of the simpler ways is to use Aitken's repeated process after having interchanged the roles of x and y. If the table is stored appropriately, the same set of instructions might be used to do either inverse interpolation or ordinary interpolation. This usefulness of Aitken's method is possible because no restriction in terms of uniform spacing of either x or y is required.

A second approach is useful if the independent variable x is of uniform spacing h. Now to find an x given a y between two tabular values, we proceed as follows: Newton's forward interpolation formula can be written as

$$y = y_0 + u\,\Delta y_0 + \sum_{k=2}^{n} \binom{u}{k} \Delta^k y_0 \tag{4.21}$$

We put equation (4.21) in the form

$$u = f(u) \tag{4.22}$$

as

$$u = \frac{y - y_0}{\Delta y_0} - \frac{1}{\Delta y_0} \sum_{k=2}^{n} \binom{u}{k} \Delta^k y_0 \tag{4.23}$$

We may iterate equation (4.23) choosing

$$u_0 = \frac{y - y_0}{\Delta y_0}$$

When the iteration converges, we find the inverse interpolated value of x by

$$x = x_0 + hu \tag{4.24}$$

EXAMPLE.   Use iterative inverse interpolation to find x when $y = 6.25$ from the table.

x	2	3	4	5	6	7	8	9	10
y	4	9	16	25	36	49	64	81	100

Solution.

x	y		
2	4		
		5	
3	9		2
		7	
4	16		2
		9	
5	25		2
		11	
6	36		2
		13	
7	49		2
		15	
8	64		2
		17	
9	81		2
		19	
10	100		

The formula is

$$u = \frac{y - y_0}{\Delta y_0} - \frac{1}{\Delta y_0} \frac{u(u - 1)}{2} \Delta^2 y_0$$

since higher differences are zero.   Now

$$u_0 = \frac{6.25 - 4}{5} = \frac{2.25}{5} = .45$$

$$u_1 = .45 - \frac{1}{5}\left[\frac{.45(.45 - 1)(2)}{2}\right] = .4995$$

$$u_2 = .45 - \frac{1}{5}\left[\frac{(.4995)(.4995 - 1)(2)}{2}\right] = .49999995$$

Since u_2 is close to u_1, we now accept from equation (4.24)

$$x = 2 + (1)(.49999995) = 2.49999995$$

Since the table is a table of squares, the result should be $x = 2.5$.

PROBLEMS

For the problems below use the following table:

x	0	1	2	3	4	5	6	7	8
y	4.500	4.000	6.250	10.80	17.50	26.29	37.13	50.00	64.90

x	9	10	11	12	13	14	15	16	17
y	81.82	100.8	121.7	144.6	169.6	196.6	225.5	256.5	289.5

x	18	19	20	21	22	23	24	25	26
y	324.5	361.4	400.4	441.4	484.4	529.4	576.4	625.3	676.3

x	27	28	29	30	31	32	33	34	35
y	729.3	784.3	841.3	900.3	961.3	1024.	1089.	1156.	1225.

x	36	37	38	39	40	41	42	43	44
y	1296.	1369.	1442.	1521.	1600.	1681.	1764.	1849.	1936.

x	45	46	47	48	49	50
y	2025.	2116.	2209.	2304.	2401.	2500.

1. Use Newton's forward formula to calculate
   (a) y when $x = 2.6$.
   (b) y when $x = 15.4$.
   (c) y when $x = 41.8$.
   (d) y when $x = 49.5$.

2. Use Newton's backward formula to calculate
   (a) y when $x = 49.5$.
   (b) y when $x = 41.8$.
   (c) y when $x = 15.4$.
   (d) y when $x = 2.6$.

3. Use Aitken's repeated process to calculate
   (a) y when $x = 5.6$.
   (b) y when $x = 9.3$.
   (c) x when $y = 17.5$.

4. Use inverse interpolation to find
   (a) x when $y = 17.5$.
   (b) x when $y = 2000$.

To check your results you may use the fact that the table was constructed from the equation

$$y = x^2 + \frac{9}{x + 2}$$

5 CURVE FITTING

5.1 INTRODUCTION

In fitting empirical data with an approximating formula there are two approaches possible. One is to have the approximating function pass through the observed points. Thus the approximating function will reproduce the original observed data exactly. Interpolating polynomials discussed in Chapter 6 have this property. The other approach is to have the approximating function retain some properties of the data, such as the shape of the curve, and to have it pass as close as possible but not necessarily through the original data points. This is usually acceptable when dealing with experimental data, which are subject to errors in reading and recording. Once the approximating formula is established, it is inserted in the program and the computer can quickly substitute whatever values are desired. In the case of interpolation an entire table would be required. The computation of points then involves a table look-up as well as a function evaluation. This is costly in machine space (memory) and in the time required for the table look-up procedure.

5.2 THE METHOD OF LEAST SQUARES

This method, developed by Legendre over one hundred and fifty years ago, has been used in statistics for many years. With the advent of digital computers it has become a useful technique for engineers and physicists as well. We find an approximating function such that the sum of the squares of the differences between the approximating function and the true function is a minimum, and we arbitrarily pick the form of the approximating function. We can then calculate the coefficients in the function.

The approximating function we have chosen may not be a good one, and this technique gives us the best of that form in the least-squares sense only. Suppose we are given the three points on the parabola (Fig. 5.1). The best straight line found by the least-squares method is the one that passes through the point $(0, \frac{2}{3})$ and is parallel to the x-axis. Obviously it is an extremely poor fit to the data. Thus several individuals might arrive at different least-squares curves for the same data. Obviously extreme care must be used in choosing an appropriate form for the approximating function.

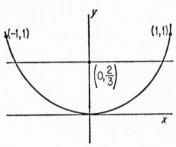

Fig. 5.1.

Assume that we have a table of points, $(x_0, y_0), (x_1, y_1), \ldots, (x_n, y_n)$ and we desire an empirical function for this data set. We will call this approximating function $g(x)$. The difference between the approximating function $g(x)$ at the point (x_i, y_i) and the actual curve may be written as

$$\varepsilon_i = g(x_i) - y_i \tag{5.1}$$

Now we compute all of these ε_i for the $(n + 1)$ data points, square, and sum to get

$$M = \sum_{i=0}^{n} [g(x_i) - y_i]^2 \tag{5.2}$$

Now we choose $g(x)$ so that it is a linear combination of suitable functions. Now

$$g(x) = C_1 g_1(x) + C_2 g_2(x) + \cdots + C_k g_k(x) \tag{5.3}$$

Now we can consider M as a function of $C_1, C_2, C_3, \ldots, C_k$. A necessary condition for a minimum is that

$$\frac{\partial M}{\partial C_1} = \frac{\partial M}{\partial C_2} = \cdots = \frac{\partial M}{\partial C_k} = 0 \tag{5.4}$$

Now

$$M = \sum_{i=0}^{n} [C_1 g_1(x_i) + C_2 g_2(x_i) + \cdots + C_k g_k(x_i) - y_i]^2$$

and, using (5.4), we have

$$\frac{\partial M}{\partial C_1} = 2 \sum_{i=0}^{n} \{[C_1 g_1(x_i) + C_2 g_2(x_i) + \cdots + C_k g_k(x_i) - y_i] g_1(x_i)\} = 0$$

$$\frac{\partial M}{\partial C_2} = 2 \sum_{i=0}^{n} \{[C_1 g_1(x_i) + C_2 g_2(x_i) + \cdots + C_k g_k(x_i) - y_i] g_2(x_i)\} = 0$$

$$\cdot$$
$$\cdot$$
$$\cdot$$ (5.5)

$$\frac{\partial M}{\partial C_k} = 2 \sum_{i=0}^{n} \{[C_1 g_1(x_i) + C_2 g_2(x_i) + \cdots + C_k g_k(x_i) - y_i] g_k(x_i)\} = 0$$

Equations (5.5) can be put into the following form:

$$C_1 \sum_{i=0}^{n} g_1^2(x_i) + C_2 \sum_{i=0}^{n} g_1(x_i)g_2(x_i) + \cdots + C_k \sum_{i=0}^{n} g_1(x_i)g_k(x_i) = \sum_{i=0}^{n} g_1(x_i)y_i$$

$$C_1 \sum_{i=0}^{n} g_1(x_i)g_2(x_i) + C_2 \sum_{i=0}^{n} g_2^2(x_i) + \cdots + C_k \sum_{i=0}^{n} g_2(x_i)g_k(x_i) = \sum_{i=0}^{n} g_2(x_i)y_i$$

$$\cdot$$
$$\cdot$$ (5.6)

$$C_1 \sum_{i=0}^{n} g_1(x_i)g_k(x_i) + C_2 \sum_{i=0}^{n} g_2(x_i)g_k(x_i) + \cdots + C_k \sum_{i=0}^{n} g_k^2(x_i) = \sum_{i=0}^{n} g_k(x_i)y_i$$

Since the summations in equations (5.6) are obtained from the data, these equations are linear equations in $C_1, C_2, \ldots, C_k$. After solving equations (5.6) simultaneously, we can substitute the values of $C_1, C_2, \ldots, C_k$ into equation (5.3) and we have our least-squares curve fit.

EXAMPLE. Fit a straight line to the data.

x	0	2	4	6	8	10
y	1.0	5.1	9.0	13.0	17.0	21.0

The form of the least-squares straight line is $y = C_0 + C_1 x$.

Solution. Substituting into equation (5.2), we have

$$M = \sum_{i=0}^{n} (C_0 + C_1 x_i - y_i)^2$$

Using (5.4), we have

$$\frac{\partial M}{\partial C_0} = 2 \sum_{i=0}^{n} (C_0 + C_1 x_i - y_i) = 0$$

$$\frac{\partial M}{\partial C_1} = 2 \sum_{i=0}^{n} (C_0 + C_1 x_i - y_i)x_i = 0$$ (5.7)

Now equations (5.7) reduce to

$$\sum_{i=0}^{n} C_0 + \sum_{i=0}^{n} C_1 x_i = \sum_{i=0}^{n} y_i$$

$$\sum_{i=0}^{n} C_0 x_i + \sum_{i=0}^{n} C_1 x_i^2 = \sum_{i=0}^{n} x_i y_i$$

(5.8)

Now $\sum_{i=0}^{n} C_0 = nC_0$, and we can factor out C_0 and C_1 in the other terms of equations (5.8) and obtain

$$nC_0 + C_1 \sum_{i=0}^{n} x_i = \sum_{i=0}^{n} y_i$$

$$C_0 \sum_{i=0}^{n} x_i + C_1 \sum_{i=0}^{n} x_i^2 = \sum_{i=0}^{n} x_i y_i$$

(5.9)

Now from the data we obtain:

$$n = 6$$

$$\sum_{i=0}^{6} x_i = 30$$

$$\sum_{i=0}^{6} y_i = 66.1$$

$$\sum_{i=0}^{6} x_i^2 = 220$$

$$\sum_{i=0}^{n} x_i y_i = 470.2$$

Now equations (5.9) become

$$6C_0 + 30C_1 = 66.1$$

$$30C_0 + 220C_1 = 470.2$$

Solving simultaneously, we obtain

$$C_0 = 1.0381$$

$$C_1 = 1.9957$$

Thus the straight-line fit is $y = 1.0381 + 1.9957x$.

The restriction that $g(x)$ be a linear combination of functions is made so that the resulting system of equations be linear in $C_1, C_2, \ldots, C_k$. Theoretically there is no reason for this restriction, but if $g(x)$ is not a linear combination of functions the resulting system of equations will not be linear and thus not easily solved.

As long as $g(x)$ is linear in its coefficients almost any function may be tried. Functions of the form

$$g(x) = \frac{C_0}{x^2} + \frac{C_1}{x} + C_2 + C_3x + C_4x^2 + \cdots + C_nx^{n-2}$$

are particularly useful. Circles, ellipses, and hyperbolas about the origin can sometimes be determined from

$$y^2 = C_1 + C_2x^2$$

Now let $Y = y^2$ and $X = x^2$; then we have

$$g(x) = Y = C_1 + C_2X$$

The values of C_1 and C_2 will be determined by the nature of the conic section.

This technique may also be used for data with more than one independent variable. The choice of an appropriate function may be difficult, and the best least-squares fit may prove useless.

It should also be noted that if there are n terms in the function $g(x)$, there must be at least n different data points given, preferably more. For less than n data points, there will be no solution to the normal equations. *Caution:* The approximating function derived by the method of least squares should not be used with x values outside the range of those used in the fitting process. In other words, $g(x)$ is only good for $x_0 \leq x \leq x_n$. Outside of these limits, $g(x)$ may produce startling results.

5.3 TRANSFORMATION OF THE DATA

The scaling and/or translation of the original data often makes the curve fitting easier or improves the accuracy. In the form

$$g(x) = y = \frac{C_0}{x} + C_1 + C_2x + C_3x^2$$

the origin would cause difficulties. In this case a transformation of the form $X = ax + b$ may be used to remove the discontinuity from the region of the observed data. For high-order polynomials a transformation that would place the data in the neighborhood of $x = 1$ would be desirable. In this way we can minimize the effect of round-off error and possible overflow or underflow.

5.4 FLOW DIAGRAM FOR LEAST-SQUARES CURVE FIT

A subroutine, which may be changed at will according to the type of approximating function, can be programmed to provide the sequence g_j and y. A sample flow chart is shown in Fig. 5.2.

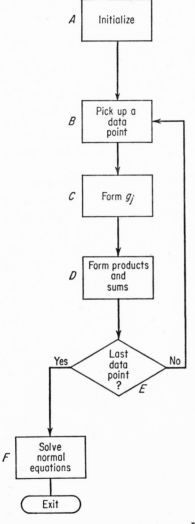

Block A: The loops of the program, based on n, are set up, and the storage locations for the sums are set to zero. Other initializing may be necessary, depending upon the idiosyncrasies of the computer used.

Block B: Get a data point (from memory, tape, drum, cards, or wherever is convenient to keep them.)

Block C: With the data point, form the terms of the approximating function, i.e., the sequence $g_1, g_2, \ldots, g_k, y$. This can be a subroutine also.

Block D: Form the products $g_1^2, g_1g_2, \ldots,$ $g_1g_k, g_1y, g_2^2, g_2g_3, \ldots, g_2g_k, g_2y, \ldots, g_k^2, g_ky,$ and add to the contents of the sums locations.

Block E: Test to see if all the data have been used. No – return to B for next point. Yes – go on to Block F. This testing may be more convenient in some cases in Block B.

Block F: Set up the form for the solution of the normal equations. All the necessary sums have been computed.

Fig. 5.2.

5.5 WHAT TYPE OF CURVE TO FIT

There are no clearly drawn criteria for determining the type of function which will best represent a data set. The following are some suggested approaches.

(1) An examination of the first few differences may indicate a polynomial.

(2) Plot the data. The equation may be obvious. Look for straight line segments and fit these separately.

(3) Look for symmetry. Symmetry with respect to the y axis suggests a polynomial of even powers only. Perhaps a translation may be necessary to achieve this. A curve symmetrical about a point suggests the translation of the origin to the point and then the fitting of an odd-powered polynomial.

(4) Look for asymptotes. A vertical asymptote may be translated outside of the realm of interest.

(5) Look for periodicity. Harmonic analysis may be indicated.

(6) Look for logarithmic or exponential tendencies by plotting on log paper.

(7) Consider breaking the curve into sections and fitting these separately. Care must be taken that the curves "match" at the end points.

5.6 CAUTION

Do not expect to differentiate your resulting least-squares curve fit. The derivatives may be calculable but meaningless, perhaps to the point of having incorrect signs.

Integration may be attempted if the function fitted is a well-behaved polynomial.

5.7 ORTHOGONAL POLYNOMIALS WITH EQUALLY SPACED DATA

In fitting a curve by least squares let us assume as our function

$$y = b_0 p_0(x) + b_1 p_1(x) + b_2 p_2(x) + \cdots + b_m p_m(x) \tag{5.10}$$

where the $p_n(x)$ are nth-degree polynomials in x. The normal equations are

$$b_0 \sum p_0^2 + b_1 \sum p_0 p_1 + \cdots + b_m \sum p_0 p_m = \sum p_0 y$$

$$b_0 \sum p_1 p_0 + b_1 \sum p_1^2 + \cdots + b_m \sum p_1 p_m = \sum p_1 y$$

$$b_0 \sum p_2 p_0 + b_1 \sum p_2 p_1 + b_2 \sum p_2^2 + \cdots + b_m \sum p_2 p_m = \sum p_2 y$$

$$\cdot$$
$$\cdot \qquad\qquad (5.11)$$
$$\cdot$$

$$b_0 \sum p_m p_0 + b_1 \sum p_m p_1 + \cdots + b_m \sum p_m^2 = \sum p_m y$$

For simplicity, the limits have been omitted from the sums. They are, in general, from 0 to n and $p_j = p_j(x)$.

If we choose a set of polynomials such that

$$\sum p_i(x) p_j(x) = 0 \qquad \text{for } i \neq j \qquad\qquad (5.12)$$

the normal equations (5.11) will reduce to

$$b_0 \sum p_0^2 + 0 + 0 + \cdots + 0 = \sum p_0 y$$

$$0 + b_1 \sum p_1^2 + \cdots + 0 = \sum p_1 y$$

$$0 + 0 + b_2 \sum p_2^2 + \cdots + 0 = \sum p_2 y$$

$$\cdot$$
$$\cdot \qquad\qquad (5.13)$$
$$\cdot$$

$$0 + 0 + 0 + \cdots + b_m \sum p_m^2 = \sum p_m y$$

Now the normal equations may be solved very simply as

$$b_0 = \frac{\sum p_0 y}{\sum p_0^2}$$

$$b_1 = \frac{\sum p_1 y}{\sum p_1^2}$$

$$b_2 = \frac{\sum p_2 y}{\sum p_2^2}$$

$$\cdots$$

or, in general,

$$b_i = \frac{\sum p_i y}{\sum p_i^2} \qquad\qquad (5.14)$$

A set of polynomials for which the conditions specified in (5.12) are satisfied are the Gram polynomials. If we transform the arguments by

$$S = \frac{x - x_0}{h} \qquad \text{where } h = x_{i+1} - x_i$$

then the values of S will be 0, 1, 2, 3, . . . , n, provided that h is constant or, in other words, the x_i are uniformly spaced. A general form for these polynomials (due to Milne) is

$$p_{m,n}(S) = \sum_{k=0}^{m} (-1)^k \binom{m}{k} \binom{m+k}{k} \frac{\binom{S}{k}}{\binom{n}{k}} \tag{5.15}$$

where m is the order of the polynomial, and $(n + 1)$ is the number of data points. The first four of these polynomials are

$$p_{0,n}(S) = 1$$

$$p_{1,n}(S) = 1 - \frac{2S}{n}$$

$$p_{2,n}(S) = 1 - \frac{6S}{n} + \frac{6S(S - 1)}{n(n - 1)}$$

$$p_{3,n}(S) = 1 - \frac{12S}{n} + \frac{3S(S - 1)}{n(n - 1)} - \frac{20S(S - 1)(S - 2)}{n(n - 1)(n - 2)}$$

Using the same notation, we have

$$\sum p_{m,n}^2 = \frac{n + m + 1}{2m + 1} \frac{\binom{m+n}{m}}{\binom{n}{m}}$$

EXAMPLE. Given the data

x	.2	.4	.6	.8	1.0	1.2
y	2.64	3.36	4.16	5.04	6.00	7.04

for which $n = 5$, we have $S = (x - .2)/.2$ and

$$p_0 = 1$$

$$p_1 = 1 - \frac{2S}{5}$$

$$p_2 = 1 - \frac{3S}{2} + \frac{3S^2}{10}$$

Now we have the table

x	S	y	p_0	yp_0	p_1	yp_1
.2	0	2.64	1	2.64	1.0	2.64
.4	1	3.36	1	3.36	.6	2.016
.6	2	4.16	1	4.16	.2	.832
.8	3	5.04	1	5.04	−.2	−1.008
1.0	4	6.00	1	6.00	−.6	−3.600
1.2	5	7.04	1	7.04	−1.0	−7.040
				28.24		−6.160

Now
$$\sum p_0^2 = 6, \quad \sum p_0 y = 28.24, \quad \sum p_1^2 = 2.8, \quad \sum p_1 y = -6.16$$

so that
$$b_0 = \frac{28.24}{6} = 4.707, \qquad b_1 = \frac{-6.160}{2.8} = -2.2$$

Fitting (5.10) as a straight line, we have
$$y = 4.707 p_0 - 2.2 p_1$$

or, substituting for p_0 and p_1, we have
$$y = 4.707(1) - 2.2 \left(1 - \frac{2S}{5}\right)$$

or
$$y = 2.507 + .88S$$

and, since $S = (x - .2)/.2$, we have
$$y = 2.507 + .88 \frac{x - .2}{.2}$$

or
$$y = 1.627 + 4.4x$$

Now we substitute x into this equation and find

x	.2	.4	.6	.8	1.0	1.2
y	2.507	3.387	4.267	5.147	6.027	6.907
observed y	2.64	3.36	4.16	5.04	6.00	7.04

Over this small range of x the values appear fairly close, but let us extend to the form $y = b_0 p_0 + b_1 p_1 + b_2 p_2$. For this we merely extend our table.

x	S	y	p_0	yp_0	p_1	yp_1	p_2	yp_2	$\bar{y}$
.2	0	2.64	1	2.64	1.0	2.640	1.0	2.640	2.640
.4	1	3.36	1	3.36	.6	2.016	−.2	−.672	3.360
.6	2	4.16	1	4.16	.2	.832	−.8	−3.328	4.161
.8	3	5.04	1	5.04	−.2	−1.008	−.8	−4.032	5.041
1.0	4	6.00	1	6.00	−.6	−3.600	−.2	−1.200	6.000
1.2	5	7.04	1	7.04	−1.0	−7.040	1.0	7.040	7.040
				28.24		−6.160		.448	

Again
$$b_0 = \frac{2.824}{6} = 4.707$$

$$b_1 = \frac{-6.160}{2.8} = -2.2$$

and
$$b_2 = \frac{.448}{3.36} \qquad \text{where } \sum p_2^2 = 3.36$$

and

$$y = 4.707p_0 - 2.2p_1 + 1.33p_2$$

Substituting, we get

$$y = 4.707 - 2.2\left(1 - \frac{2S}{5}\right) + .133\left(1 - \frac{3S}{2} + \frac{3S^2}{10}\right)$$

or

$$y = 2.64 + .681S + .04S^2$$

Returning to the variable x by $y = (x - .2)/.2$, we have

$$v = 1.999 + 3.005x + x^2 \tag{5.16}$$

In the table above $\bar{y}$ has been computed from equation (5.16).

In this example we have demonstrated the ease with which this method can be extended to higher-degree polynomials.

PROBLEMS

For each of the following, graph the data shown, pick a type of curve, and fit by the least-squares method.

1.

x	0.	1.	2.	3.	4.	5.	6.	7.
y	1.35	−2.648	−.6480	7.352	21.35	41.35	67.35	99.35

x	8.	9.	10.	11.	12.	13.	14.	15.
y	137.4	181.4	231.4	287.4	349.4	417.4	491.4	571.4

x	16.	17.	18.	19.	20.	21.	22.	23.
y	651.4	749.3	847.3	951.3	1061.	1177.	1299.	1427.

x	24.	25.	26.	27.	28.	29.
y	1561.	1701.	1847.	1999.	2157.	2321.

2.

x	0.	1.	2.	3.	4.	5.	6.	7.	8.	9.
y	0.	2.84	4.90	6.14	7.24	9.04	11.7	14.6	16.9	18.4

x	10.	11.	12.	13.	14.	15.	16.	17.	18.	19.
y	19.4	21.0	23.5	26.4	28.9	30.6	31.7	33.1	35.2	38.1

x	20.	21.	22.	23.
y	40.9	42.8	43.9	45.2

3.

x	4.	5.	6.	7.	8.	9.	10.	11.	12.	13.
y	16.8	25.6	36.7	49.5	64.4	81.4	100.	121.	144.	169.

x	14.	15.	16.
y	196.	226.	257.

4.

x	1.	2.	3.	4.	5.	6.	7.	8.	9.	10.
y	.266	.362	.496	.603	.732	.856	.987	1.12	1.26	1.41

x	11.	12.	13.	14.	15.	16.
y	1.56	1.71	1.87	2.04	2.22	2.40

6 NUMERICAL INTEGRATION

6.1 INTRODUCTION

In this chapter we will deal with integrals of the type

$$\int_a^b f(x)\,dx$$

Many integrals of this type can be integrated in terms of elementary functions. Others such as

$$\int_0^1 e^{-x^2}\,dx$$

cannot be so integrated. Nevertheless, numerous applications require numerical values for such integrals. The consideration of techniques for getting good approximations to these integrals is the purpose of this chapter.

Consider the integral

$$\int_a^b f(x)\,dx$$

If a and b are constants, the integral when evaluated is a constant and may be considered as the area under the curve $y = f(x)$ between $x = a$ and $x = b$ as in Fig. 6.1. Recalling that the definite integral is a summation process, we could insert a large number of rectangles under the curve and sum as in Fig. 6.2. That is, the integral will be approximated as

$$\sum_{i=1}^m y_i\,\Delta x_i$$

A large number of rectangles may be inserted and possibly good results achieved. However, there are two drawbacks to this approach. They are: (a) round-off error, (b) running time on the computer.

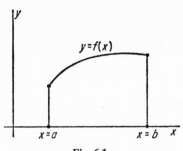

Fig. 6.1.

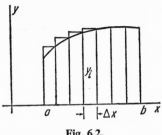

Fig. 6.2.

Round-off error occurs all the time but when many calculations are performed and the results added, the errors of this type may yield poor results.

The calculation of all the sums required is time-consuming even on a computer, and methods which would yield accurate results in a shorter period of time would be preferred. (Computer time on large computers may cost in the neighborhood of $600 an hour.)

6.2 NEWTON-COTES CLOSED-TYPE FORMULAS

Another approach is to replace $f(x)$ in the integral

$$\int_{x_0}^{x_n} f(x)\, dx$$

by an integrable function such as a polynomial which passes through several points on the curve $y = f(x)$ in the interval $x_0 \leq x \leq x_n$. In general, the higher the degree of the polynomial the better can be the fit. We will not consider above a sixth-degree polynomial, however.

In the integral

$$\int_{x_0}^{x_n} f(x)\, dx$$

replace x by $x = x_0 + hu$ so that $dx = h\, du$ and

$$\int_{x_0}^{x_n} f(x)\, dx = h \int_0^n f(x_0 + hu)\, du$$

where the limits are replaced as follows:

At the lower limit x_0:

$$x_0 = x_0 + hu \quad \text{or} \quad hu = 0, \quad u = 0$$

At the upper limit:

$$x_n = x_0 + hu \quad \text{or} \quad u = \frac{x_n - x_0}{h}$$

Recalling Newton's forward formula, with equally spaced ordinates

$$x_n - x_0 = nh \qquad (n \text{ intervals})$$

and

$$u = \frac{x_n - x_0}{h} = \frac{nh}{n} = n$$

Now replace $f(x_0 + hu)$ by Newton's forward formula and we have

$$\int_{x_0}^{x_n} f(x)\, dx = h \int_0^n f(x_0 + hu)\, du$$

$$= h \int_0^n \left(y_0 + u\, \Delta y_0 + \binom{u}{2} \Delta^2 y_0 + \binom{u}{3} \Delta^3 y_0 + \cdots \right) du \quad (6.1)$$

Recalling that if $(n + 1)$st and higher-order differences are zero, the function is a polynomial of degree n, we can truncate Newton's forward formula after first differences and fit a straight line, after second differences and fit a parabola, after third differences and fit a cubic.

For the straight-line fit we integrate (6.1) from $n = 0$ to $n = 1$ and truncate after first differences as follows:

$$\int_{x_0}^{x_1} f(x)\, dx = h \int_0^1 (y_0 + u\, \Delta y_0)\, du = h \left[u y_0 + \frac{u^2}{2} \Delta y_0 \right]_0^1$$

$$= h \left[y_0 + \frac{1}{2} \Delta y_0 \right] \qquad (6.2)$$

Now $\Delta y_0 = y_1 - y_0$ and

$$\int_{x_0}^{x_1} f(x)\, dx = h \left[y_0 + \frac{1}{2}(y_1 - y_0) \right] = \frac{h}{2} [y_0 + y_1]$$

Now

$$\int_{x_0}^{x_1} f(x)\, dx = \frac{h}{2} [y_0 + y_1]$$

which is the trapezoidal rule. If n intervals are to be used instead of one, we have

$$\int_{x_0}^{x_n} f(x)\, dx = \frac{h}{2} [y_0 + y_1] + \frac{h}{2} [y_1 + y_2] + \frac{h}{2} [y_2 + y_3] + \cdots + \frac{h}{2} [y_{n-1} + y_n]$$

or

$$\int_{x_0}^{x_n} f(x)\, dx = \frac{h}{2} [y_0 + 2y_1 + 2y_2 + 2y_3 + \cdots + 2y_{n-1} + y_n] \quad (6.3)$$

(All the coefficients of the y_i are 2's except the first and last.) The trapezoidal rule gives good results only when second differences are negligible. Its advantages are simplicity and the fact that any number of intervals may be used.

If now we truncate (6.1) after second differences and integrate over two intervals:

$$\int_{x_0}^{x_2} f(x)\, dx = h \int_0^2 \left[y + u\,\Delta y_0 + \frac{u(u-1)}{2}\Delta^2 y_0 \right] du$$

$$\int_{x_0}^{x_2} f(x)\, dx = h \left[u y_0 + \frac{u^2}{2}\Delta y_0 + \left(\frac{u^3}{6} - \frac{u^2}{4}\right)\Delta^2 y_0 \right]_0^2$$

where

$$\Delta y_0 = y_1 - y_0$$

$$\Delta^2 y_0 = y_2 - 2y_1 + y_0$$

$$\int_{x_0}^{x_2} f(x)\, dx = h \left[2y_0 + 2\Delta y_0 + \left(\frac{4}{3} - 1\right)\Delta^2 y_0 \right]$$

$$= h \left[2y_0 + 2(y_1 - y_0) + \frac{1}{3}(y_2 - 2y_1 + y_0) \right]$$

$$\int_{x_0}^{x_2} f(x)\, dx = h \left[\frac{1}{3} y_0 + \frac{4}{3} y_1 + \frac{1}{3} y_2 \right] = \frac{h}{3}[y_0 + 4y_1 + y_2] \qquad (6.4)$$

This is known as Simpson's rule. Noting that it was derived on the basis of two intervals, we may extend it to any *even* number of intervals as follows:

$$\int_{x_0}^{x_n} f(x)\, dx$$

$$= \frac{h}{3}[y_0 + 4y_1 + y_2] + \frac{h}{3}[y_2 + 4y_3 + y_4] + \cdots + \frac{h}{3}[y_{n-2} + 4y_{n-1} + y_n]$$

or

$$\int_{x_0}^{x_n} f(x)\, dx$$

$$= \frac{h}{3}[y_0 + 4y_1 + 2y_2 + 4y_3 + 2y_4 + 4y_5 + 2y_6 + \cdots + 2y_{n-2} + 4y_{n-1} + y_n]$$

Simpson's rule is probably the most widely used quadrature formula. On the basis of our derivation we can expect that it will yield exact results for a polynomial of degree two. However, it not only does this but also yields exact results for cubics as is shown below.

$$\int_{-h}^{h} (ax^3 + bx^2 + cx + d)\, dx = \frac{2bh^3}{3} + 2dh = \frac{h}{3}[2bh^2 + 6d]$$

This is the exact result by direct integration. If the integral is not over the limits $-h$ to h, it may be translated so that it does conform to these limits. Such translation does not affect the area or the corresponding integral. Now, applying Simpson's rule with $x_0 = -h$, $x_1 = 0$, and $x_2 = h$, we have

$$y_0 = -ah^3 + bh^2 - ch + d$$

$$4y_1 = \qquad\qquad\qquad\quad 4d$$

$$y_2 = \quad ah^3 + bh^2 + ch + d$$

or

$$\frac{h}{3}\left[y_0 + 4y_1 + y_2\right] = \frac{h}{3}\left[2bh^2 + 6d\right]$$

which is the result by integrating. Thus Simpson's rule gives exact results for cubics. The rule obtained by truncating Newton's forward after third differences is seldom used, as it does not yield any more accurate results than Simpson's rule. However, we list it for information:

$$\int_{x_0}^{x_3} f(x)\,dx = \frac{3}{8}h[y_0 + 3y_1 + 3y_2 + y_3] \tag{6.5}$$

It is known as Simpson's 3/8 rule.

Next, truncating after fourth differences, we obtain the following:

$$\int_{x_0}^{x_4} f(x)\,dx = \frac{2h}{45}\left[7y_0 + 32y_1 + 12y_2 + 32y_3 + 7y_4\right]$$

This is known as Boole's rule and may be used with multiples of four intervals.
 Going to

$$\int_{x_0}^{x_6} f(x)\,dx$$

truncating Newton's forward after sixth differences, and integrating, we obtain

$$\int_{x_0}^{x_6} f(x)\,dx$$

$$= h\left[6y_0 + 18\,\Delta y_0 + 27\,\Delta^2 y_0 + 24\,\Delta^3 y_0 + \frac{123}{10}\,\Delta^4 y_0 + \frac{33}{10}\,\Delta^5 y_0 + \frac{41}{140}\,\Delta^6 y_0\right]$$

This yields a scheme in which the coefficients of the y_i are not symmetric as in previous rules. However, we can achieve a better-looking (if less accurate) result by replacing $\frac{41}{140}\,\Delta^6 y_0$ by $\frac{42}{140}\,\Delta^6 y_0 = \frac{3}{10}\,\Delta^6 y_0$. Thus:

$$\int_{x_0}^{x_6} f(x)\, dx$$

$$= h\left[6y_0 + 18\,\Delta y_0 + 27\,\Delta^2 y_0 + 24\,\Delta^3 y_0 + \frac{123}{10}\,\Delta^4 y_0 + \frac{33}{10}\,\Delta^5 y_0 + \frac{3}{10}\,\Delta^6 y_0 \right]$$

$$I_w = \frac{3h}{10}\left[y_0 + 5y_1 + y_2 + 6y_3 + y_4 + 5y_5 + y_6 \right].$$

This is known as Weddle's rule. Since we changed the term involving sixth differences, it does not fit a sixth-degree polynomial. It does fit exactly polynomials of degree five or less. Also, Weddle's rule requires the data in groups of six intervals. Thus for 12 intervals:

$$I_w = \frac{3h}{10}\left[y_0 + 5y_1 + y_2 + 6y_3 + y_4 + 5y_5 + 2y_6 \right.$$

$$\left. + 5y_7 + y_8 + 6y_9 + y_{10} + 5y_{11} + y_{12} \right]$$

EXAMPLE.   Compute $\int_0^{.6} x^4\, dx$ using $h = .1$.

Solution.   The trapezoidal rule, Simpson's rule, and Weddle's rule apply $(y = x^4)$.

x	0	.1	.2	.3	.4	.5	.6
y	0	.0001	.0016	.0081	.0256	.0625	.1296

$$I_T = \frac{.1}{2}\left[0 + 2(.0001) + 2(.0016) + 2(.0081) + 2(.0256) + 2(.0625) + .1296 \right]$$

$$I_T = \underline{.01627}$$

$$I_S = \frac{.1}{3}\left[0 + 4(.0001) + 2(.0016) + 4(.0081) + 2(.0256) + 4(.0625) + .1296 \right]$$

$$I_S = \underline{.01556}$$

$$I_W = \frac{3(.1)}{10}\left[0 + 5(.0001) + .0016 + 6(.0081) + .0256 + 5(.0625) + .1296 \right]$$

$$I_W = \underline{.015552}$$

The exact value of the integral is

$$\int_0^{.6} x^4\, dx = \underline{.015552}.$$

Notice that Weddle's rule gives exact results, since the function is only fourth-degree and Weddle's rule gives exact results for quintics.

6.3 METHOD OF UNDETERMINED COEFFICIENTS

We shall derive the trapezoidal rule.

The integral

$$\int_{x_0}^{x_1} y\, dx$$

is desired as a linear combination of y_0 and y_1 such that the formula obtained is exact for $y = (x - x_0)^n$ for $n = 0, 1$. Thus

$$\int_{x_0}^{x_1} y\, dx = C_0 y_0 + C_1 y_1 \tag{6.6}$$

We have two constants to determine and two conditions to use, namely that the result be exact for $n = 0$ and $n = 1$. For $n = 0$, $y = 1$ and (6.6) becomes

$$\int_{x_0}^{x_1} dx = C_0 + C_1 \quad \text{or} \quad x_1 - x_0 = C_0 + C_1$$

but $x_1 - x_0 = h$, so

$$C_0 + C_1 = h \tag{6.7}$$

For $n = 1$

$$\int_{x_0}^{x_1} (x - x_0)\, dx = C_0(0) + C_1(x_1 - x_0)$$

but again $x_1 - x_0 = h$

$$\frac{(x - x_0)^2}{2}\bigg]_{x_0}^{x_2} = C_1 h, \qquad \frac{(x^1 - x_0)^2}{2} = C_1 h$$

and $x_1 - x_0 = 2h$, so

$$\frac{h^2}{2} = C_1 h, \qquad C_1 = \frac{h}{2}$$

and, referring to (6.7),

$$C_0 + \frac{h}{2} = h \quad \text{and} \quad C_0 = \frac{h}{2}$$

so that (6.6) becomes

$$\int_{x_0}^{x_1} y\, dx = \frac{h}{2} y_0 + \frac{h}{2} y_1 = \frac{h}{2}(y_0 + y_1)$$

which is recognized as the trapezoidal rule.

Let us derive Simpson's rule in the same manner. We wish to express

$$\int_{x_0}^{x_2} y\, dx$$

as a linear combination of y_0, y_1, y_2, so we write

$$\int_{x_0}^{x_2} y\, dx = c_0 y_0 + c_1 y_1 + c_2 y_2 \tag{6.8}$$

where the c_i are undetermined coefficients. Since we have *three* constants at our disposal, we can expect our formula to be exact for polynomials up through degree *two*. In particular, it must be exact for the cases $y = 1$, $y = x - x_0$, $y = (x - x_0)^2$. For these three cases, then, we have (noting that $x_1 - x_0 = h$, $x_2 - x_0 = 2h$)

$$\int_{x_0}^{x_2} dx = x_2 - x_0 = 2h = c_0 + c_1 + c_2$$

$$\int_{x_0}^{x_2} (x - x_0)\, dx = \frac{(x - x_0)^2}{2}\Big]_{x_0}^{x_2} = 2h^2 = 0 + c_1 h + 2c_2 h$$

$$\int_{x_0}^{x_2} (x - x_0)^2\, dx = \frac{(x - x_0)^3}{3}\Big]_{x_0}^{x_2} = \frac{8h^3}{3} = 0 + c_1 h^2 + 4c_2 h^2$$

Hence, we obtain the system of three equations in three unknowns c_i:

$$c_0 + c_1 + c_2 = 2h$$

$$c_1 + 2c_2 = 2h$$

$$c_1 + 4c_2 = \frac{8}{3} h$$

whose solution is seen to be

$$c_0 = \frac{h}{3}; \qquad c_1 = \frac{4h}{3}; \qquad c_2 = \frac{h}{3}$$

Hence (6.8) becomes

$$\int_{x_0}^{x_2} y\, dx = \frac{h}{3} (y_0 + 4y_1 + y_2)$$

as we saw in (6.4).

The method of undetermined coefficients can also be used to find formulas by which we express functional values as a linear combination of other functional values and of derivatives. For example, we can use it to obtain rules such as

$$y_4 \simeq y_0 + \frac{4h}{3} (2y_1' - y_2' + 2y_3')$$

and

$$\int_{x_0}^{x_2} y\, dx = \frac{h}{15} (7y_0 + 16y_1 + 7y_2) + \frac{h^2}{15} (y_0' - y_2')$$

6.4 ERRORS WITH NEWTON-COTES CLOSED FORMULAS

Some general discussion of the error bounds of the three formulas should be of interest. Let $F(x) = \int f(x)\, dx$. Then

$$I = \int_{x_0}^{x_0+h} f(x)\, dx = F(x_0 + h) - F(x_0)$$

From the trapezoidal rule we have

$$I_T = \frac{h}{2}\,[f(x_0) + f(x_0 + h)] = \frac{h}{2}\,(y_0 + y_1)$$

and we define the error of the method by

$$E_T = I_T - I = \frac{h}{2}\,[f(x_0) + f(x_0 + h)] - [F(x_0 + h) - F(x_0)]$$

Expanding $F(x_0 + h)$ and $f(x_0 + h)$ by Taylor series, and noting that $F'(x) = f(x)$, we have

$$E_T = \frac{h}{2}\left[2f(x_0) + hf'(x_0) + \frac{h^2}{2!}f''(x_0) + \cdots \right]$$

$$- h\left[f(x_0) + \frac{h}{2!}f(x_0) + \frac{h^2}{3!}f''(x_0) + \cdots \right]$$

$$= \frac{h^3}{12}f''(x_0) + \text{higher powers of } h$$

The principal part of the error is thus $(h^3/12)f''(x_0)$. When using the trapezoidal rule over n such intervals, spanning a range of length nh, we have

$$E_T \simeq \frac{nh^3}{12}f''(x_p) = \frac{nh}{12}f''(x_p)h^2$$

where $f''(x_p)$ is an average value of the second derivative on the interval $x_0 \le x \le x_{0+h}$. The error is said to be of order h^2.

The error via Simpson's rule may be found in a similar fashion.

$$I = \int_{a}^{a+2h} f(x)\, dx = F(a + 2h) - F(a)$$

(The exact result.)

$$I_S = \frac{h}{3}\,[f(a) + 4f(a + h) + f(a + 2h)] \tag{6.9}$$

(The Simpson's rule approximation.)

$$f(a + h) = f(a) + f'(a)(a + h - a) + f''(a)\frac{h^2}{2!}$$

$$+ f'''(a)\frac{h^3}{3!} + f^{\text{iv}}(a)\frac{h^4}{4!} \cdots$$

$$f(a + 2h) = f(a) + f'(a)(a + 2h - a) + f''(a)\frac{4h^2}{2!}$$

$$+ f'''(a)\frac{8h^3}{3!} + f^{iv}(a)\frac{16h^4}{4!} + f^{v}(a)\frac{32h^5}{5!}$$

$$F(a + 2h) - F(a) = F'(a)(2h) + F''(a)2h^2 + F'''(a)\frac{4h^3}{3}$$

$$+ \frac{2F^{iv}(a)h^4}{3} + \frac{32F^{v}(a)h^5}{5!} + \cdots$$

$$F'(x) = f(x)$$

$$F''(x) = f'(x)$$

$$F'''(x) = f''(x)$$

$$F^{iv}(x) = f'''(x)$$

Since $F(x)$ is the integral of $f(x)$, now we have

$$F(a + 2h) - F(a) = 2hf(a) + 2f'(a)h^2 + \frac{4}{3}f''(a)h^3 + \frac{2}{3}f'''(a)h^4 + \cdots$$

replacing in (6.9).

$$I_S = \frac{h}{3}[f(a)] + 4\left[f(a) + f'(a)h + f''(a)\frac{h^2}{2} + f'''(a)\frac{h^3}{6} + f^{iv}(a)\frac{h^4}{24} + \cdots\right]$$

$$+ \left[f(a) + 2f'(a)h + 2f''(a)h^2 + \frac{4}{3}f'''(a)h^3 + \frac{2}{3}f^{iv}(a)h^4 + \cdots\right]$$

or

$$I_S = \frac{h}{3}\left[6f(a) + 6f'(a)h + 4f''(a)h^2 + 2f'''(a)h^3 + \frac{5}{6}f^{iv}(a)h^4 + \cdots\right]$$

The error via Simpson's rule is

$$E_S = I - I_S = 2f(a)h + 2f'(a)h^2 + \frac{4}{3}f''(a)h^3 + \frac{2}{3}f'''(a)h^4 + \frac{4}{15}f^{iv}(a)h^5 + \cdots$$

$$- 2f(a)h - 2f'(a)h^2 - \frac{4}{3}f''(a)h^3 - \frac{2}{3}f'''(a)h^4$$

$$- \frac{5}{18}f^{iv}(a)h^5 + \cdots$$

$$E_S = -\frac{1}{90}f^{iv}(a)h^5 + \cdots$$

So we see that the major part of the error is $-\frac{1}{90}f^{\text{iv}}(a)h^5$. If we integrate across n intervals, the error term is

$$-\frac{nh}{90}f^{\text{iv}}(x_p)h^4, \qquad x_0 \leq x_p \leq x_n$$

The order is h^4.

A similar process for Weddle's rule yields order h^6. The formulas mentioned thus far are collected here for reference together with error terms.

Trapezoidal rule:

$$\int_{x_0}^{x_1} f(x)\,dx = \frac{h}{2}\left[y_0 + y_1\right] - \frac{h^3}{12}f''(x_p) \qquad\qquad x_0 \leq x_p \leq x_1$$

Simpson's rule:

$$\int_{x_0}^{x_2} f(x)\,dx = \frac{h}{3}\left[y_0 + 4y_1 + y_2\right] - \frac{1}{90}h^5 f^{\text{iv}}(x_p) \qquad\qquad x_0 \leq x_p \leq x_2$$

Simpson's 3/8 rule:

$$\int_{x_0}^{x_3} f(x)\,dx = \frac{3h}{8}\left[y_0 + 3y_1 + 3y_2 + y_3\right] - \frac{3}{80}h^5 f^{\text{iv}}(x_p) \qquad x_0 \leq x_p \leq x_3$$

Boole's rule:

$$\int_{x_0}^{x_4} f(x)\,dx = \frac{2h}{45}\left[7y_0 + 32y_1 + 12y_2 + 32y_3 + 7y_4\right] - \frac{8h^7}{945}f^{\text{iv}}(x_p)$$

$$x_0 \leq x_p \leq x_4$$

Weddle's rule:

$$\int_{x_0}^{x_6} f(x)\,dx = \frac{3h}{10}\left[y_0 + 5y_1 + y_2 + 6y_3 + y_4 + 5y_5 + y_6\right] + \frac{h^7}{140}f^{\text{iv}}(x_p)$$

$$x_0 \leq x_p \leq x_6$$

6.5 GAUSS' INTEGRATION FORMULA

With the Newton-Cotes formulas applied to an odd number n of equally spaced ordinates (e.g., Simpson's rule), an exact result is obtained if the ordinates are those of a polynomial of degree n or less. Gauss posed the question of whether a numerical integration formula can be obtained which gives an exact result for polynomials of degree greater than n. He found that this is possible if one is willing to sacrifice whatever advantage equally spaced ordinates might provide. The resulting formulas, applied to n selectively spaced ordinates, give exact answers when the integrated function is a polynomial of degree not exceeding $2n - 1$.

The choice of spacing of these ordinates requires an acquaintance with Legendre polynomials. The Legendre polynomials are solutions of the Legendre equation:

$$(1 - x^2)y'' - 2xy' + n(n + 1)y = 0 \tag{6.10}$$

The polynomials are of the form

$$y = P_n(x) = \frac{1}{2^n n!} \frac{d^n}{dx^n} (x^2 - 1)^n \tag{6.11}$$

This is the Rodrigues' formula for the Legendre polynomials. That (6.11) is a solution of (6.10) may be seen by direct substitution. The first several of these polynomials are:

$$P_0(x) = 1$$

$$P_1(x) = x$$

$$P_2(x) = \frac{3}{2} x^2 - \frac{1}{2}$$

$$P_3(x) = \frac{5}{2} x^3 - \frac{3}{2} x$$

$$P_4(x) = \frac{35}{8} x^4 - \frac{15}{4} x^2 + \frac{3}{8}$$

An important property of the Legendre polynomials which we will now establish is that they are orthogonal on the interval $(-1, 1)$; that is,

$$\int_{-1}^{1} P_n(x)P_m(x) \, dx = 0 \qquad \text{for } m \neq n$$

Consider the Legendre equations

$$(1 - x^2)y'' - 2xy' + n(n + 1)y = 0 \tag{6.12}$$

$$(1 - x^2)y'' - 2xy' + m(m + 1)y = 0 \tag{6.13}$$

Since $P_n(x)$ (which we shall write as P_n) is a solution of (6.12), we have

$$(1 - x^2)P_n'' - 2xP_n' + n(n + 1)P_n = 0 \tag{6.14}$$

and since similarly $P_m(x)$ (written as P_m) is a solution of (6.13), we obtain

$$(1 - x^2)P_m'' - 2xP_m' + m(m + 1)P_m = 0 \tag{6.15}$$

Multiplying (6.14) by P_m and (6.15) by P_n,

$$P_m[(1 - x^2)P_n'' - 2xP_n' + n(n + 1)P_n] = 0 \tag{6.16}$$

$$P_n[(1 - x^2)P_m'' - 2xP_m' + m(m + 1)P_m] = 0 \tag{6.17}$$

Let us (in order to simplify our work) pick

$$R(x) = P'_n P_m - P_n P'_m \tag{6.18}$$

so that

$$R'(x) = P'_n P'_m + P''_n P_m - P_n P''_m - P'_n P'_m$$

or

$$R'(x) = P''_n P_m - P_n P''_m \tag{6.19a}$$

Subtracting equation (6.17) from equation (6.16), we now have

$$(1 - x^2)[P''_n P_m - P_n P''_m] - 2x[P'_n P_m - P_n P'_m] + n(n + 1)P_n P_m$$
$$- m(m + 1)P_m P_n = 0 \tag{6.19b}$$

Simplifying equation (6.19b) with the aid of equations (6.19a) and (6.18),

$$(1 - x^2)R'(x) - 2xR(x) + [n(n + 1) - m(m + 1)]P_m P_n = 0 \tag{6.20}$$

The first two terms of equation (6.20) may be written as follows:

$$(1 - x^2)R'(x) - 2xR(x) = \frac{d}{dx}[(1 - x^2)R(x)]$$

(recalling the product rule of differentiation) so that equation (6.20) may be written as

$$\frac{d}{dx}[(1 - x^2)R(x)] + [n(n + 1) - m(m + 1)]P_m P_n = 0 \tag{6.21}$$

Now we integrate the equation over the limits $(-1, 1)$:

$$\int_{-1}^{1} \frac{d}{dx}[(1 - x^2)R(x)]\, dx + [n(n + 1) - m(m + 1)] \int_{-1}^{1} P_m P_n\, dx = 0 \tag{6.22}$$

or

$$(1 - x^2)R(x)\Big]_{-1}^{1} + [n(n + 1) - m(m + 1)] \int_{-1}^{1} P_m P_n\, dx = 0 \tag{6.23}$$

The first term of equation (6.23) goes to zero so that

$$[n(n + 1) - m(m + 1)] \int_{-1}^{1} P_m(x)P_n(x)\, dx = 0$$

(reverting to usual form). Since $m \neq n$,

$$\int_{-1}^{1} P_m(x)P_n(x)\, dx = 0$$

or, in other words, the Legendre polynomials are orthogonal on the interval $(-1, 1)$. Other interesting and useful properties of the Legendre polynomials are:

(a) $\int_{-1}^{1} P_m(x)x^n\, dx = 0$ for all nonnegative $n < m$.

(b) The Legendre polynomials consist of either all odd powers of x or all even powers of x.

(c) The zeros of $P_m(x)$ are all real and distinct and lie in the interval $(-1, 1)$.

The Gaussian quadrature formulas are of the form

$$\int_{-1}^{1} f(x)\, dx = \sum_{i=1}^{n} C_i f(x_i) \tag{6.24}$$

The n values of the C's and the n values of the x's constitute $2n$ quantities which must be determined. These $2n$ quantities can be determined so that the Gaussian quadrature formulas give exact results for polynomials of degree $n = 1, 2, \ldots, 2n - 1$. We shall illustrate the derivation for the case $n = 2$.

It is necessary to determine two abscissas x_1 and x_2 and two weights C_1 and C_2 so that

$$\int_{-1}^{1} f(x)\, dx = C_1 f(x_1) + C_2 f(x_2) \tag{6.25}$$

[merely equation (6.24) for the case $n = 2$]. This equation must be exact for the cases

$$f(x) = 1 \tag{6.26a}$$

$$f(x) = x \tag{6.26b}$$

$$f(x) = x^2 \tag{6.26c}$$

$$f(x) = x^3 \tag{6.26d}$$

Substituting equations (6.26) into equation (6.25), we obtain

$$\int_{-1}^{1} dx = C_1 + C_2 \tag{6.27a}$$

$$\int_{-1}^{1} x\, dx = C_1 x_1 + C_2 x_2 \tag{6.27b}$$

$$\int_{-1}^{1} x^2\, dx = C_1 x_1^2 + C_2 x_2^2 \tag{6.27c}$$

$$\int_{-1}^{1} x^3\, dx = C_1 x_1^3 + C_2 x_2^3 \tag{6.27d}$$

To solve this system of four equations we make use of the Legendre polynomial properties.

We multiply equation (6.27c) by $\frac{3}{2}$, equation (6.27a) by $\frac{1}{2}$.

$$\int_{-1}^{1} \tfrac{3}{2} x^2\, dx = C_1[\tfrac{3}{2} x_1^2] + C_2[\tfrac{3}{2} x_2^2] \tag{6.28}$$

$$\int_{-1}^{1} \tfrac{1}{2}\, dx = C_1[+\tfrac{1}{2}] + C_2[\tfrac{1}{2}] \tag{6.29}$$

Now we subtract equation (6.29) from (6.28).

$$\int_{-1}^{1} (\tfrac{3}{2}x^2 - \tfrac{1}{2}) \, dx = C_1[\tfrac{3}{2}x_1^2 - \tfrac{1}{2}] + C_2[\tfrac{3}{2}x_2^2 - \tfrac{1}{2}] \tag{6.30}$$

Recalling that $P_2(x) = \tfrac{3}{2}x^2 - \tfrac{1}{2}$ and $P_0(x) = 1$, equation (6.30) becomes

$$\int_{-1}^{1} P_2(x)P_0(x) \, dx = C_1[P_2(x_1)] + C_2[P_2(x_2)]$$

or, from the orthogonality property,

$$C_1P_2(x_1) + C_2P_2(x_2) = 0 \tag{6.31}$$

The same procedure for equations (6.27d) and (6.27b) yields

$$\int_{-1}^{1} \tfrac{3}{2}x^3 \, dx = C_1x_1[\tfrac{3}{2}x_1^2] + C_2x_2[\tfrac{3}{2}x_2^2] \tag{6.32}$$

$$\int_{-1}^{1} \tfrac{1}{2}x \, dx = C_1x_1[\tfrac{1}{2}] + C_2x_2[\tfrac{1}{2}] \tag{6.33}$$

Now, subtracting,

$$\int_{-1}^{1} (\tfrac{3}{2}x^3 - \tfrac{1}{2}x) \, dx = C_1x_1[\tfrac{3}{2}x_1^2 - \tfrac{1}{2}] + C_2x_2[\tfrac{3}{2}x_2^2 - \tfrac{1}{2}]$$

or

$$\int_{-1}^{1} (\tfrac{3}{2}x^2 - \tfrac{1}{2})x \, dx = C_1x_1[\tfrac{3}{2}x_1^2 - \tfrac{1}{2}] + C_2x_2[\tfrac{3}{2}x_2^2 - \tfrac{1}{2}] \tag{6.34}$$

Noting that the left-hand side of equation (6.34) is

$$\int_{-1}^{1} (\tfrac{3}{2}x^2 - \tfrac{1}{2})x \, dx = \int_{-1}^{1} P_2(x)P_1(x) \, dx = 0$$

we have

$$C_1x_1P_1(x_1) + C_2x_2P_2(x_2) = 0 \tag{6.35}$$

Now the system of equations

$$C_1P_2(x_1) + C_2P_2(x_2) = 0$$

$$C_1x_1P_2(x_1) + C_2x_2P_2(x_2) = 0$$

will be satisfied for any choice of C_1 and C_2 if we choose x_1 and x_2 to be the zeros of $P_2(x)$. Since $P_2(x) = \tfrac{3}{2}x^2 - \tfrac{1}{2}$, we obtain the zeros of $P_2(x)$ by solving $\tfrac{3}{2}x^2 - \tfrac{1}{2} = 0$, obtaining $x_1 = -\sqrt{3}/3$ and $x_2 = +\sqrt{3}/3$. Substituting these into equations (6.27a) and (6.27b),

$$\int_{-1}^{1} dx = C_1 + C_2 \quad \text{or} \quad C_1 + C_2 = 2$$

$$\int_{-1}^{1} x \, dx = C_1\left(\frac{-\sqrt{3}}{3}\right) + C_2\left(\frac{+\sqrt{3}}{3}\right)$$

or

$$0 = \frac{-\sqrt{3}}{3} C_1 + \frac{\sqrt{3}}{3} C_2 = 0$$

which yields

$$C_1 = C_2 = 1.$$

Thus we have the Gaussian quadrature formula

$$\int_{-1}^{1} f(x)\, dx = f\left(\frac{-\sqrt{3}}{3}\right) + f\left(\frac{\sqrt{3}}{3}\right)$$

which is merely equation (6.25) after substitution of the appropriate values for C_1, C_2, x_1, and x_2. This is a two-ordinate scheme which is exact for polynomials of degree three. Note that the limits must be from $x = -1$ to $x = 1$.

Formulas for $n = 3, 4, \ldots$ can be derived in a similar manner. In all cases, the abscissas x_i and their corresponding weights c_i are symmetric about the midpoint $x = 0$. These are given in Table 6.1.

Table 6.1

n	Weights (C_i)	Abscissas (x_i)
2	1.	0.5773502692
	1.	−0.5773502692
3	0.888888889	0.0
	0.555555556	0.7745966692
	0.555555556	−0.7745966692
4	0.6521451549	0.3399810436
	0.6521451549	−0.3399810436
	0.3478548451	0.8611363116
	0.3478548451	−0.8611363116
5	0.5688888889	0.
	0.4786286705	0.5384693101
	0.4786286705	−0.5384693101
	0.2369268851	0.9061798459
	0.2369268851	−0.9061798459

Recalling that the Gaussian quadrature method is of the form

$$\int_{-1}^{1} f(x)\, dx = \sum_{i=1}^{n} C_i f(x_i)$$

we note that the integral must be such that the limits are $(-1, 1)$. This can be accomplished with a transformation of variables

$$\int_a^b f(X)\, dX = \frac{b-a}{2} \int_{-1}^{1} f\left(\frac{b-a}{2} x + \frac{b+a}{2}\right) \tag{6.36}$$

where

$$X = \frac{b-a}{2} x + \frac{b+a}{2} \tag{6.37}$$

and

$$dX = \frac{b-a}{2}\, dx$$

The inverse transformation is

$$x = \frac{2X - (a+b)}{b-a}$$

As an illustrative example, let us again evaluate

$$I = \int_0^{\pi} \sin t\, dt$$

using five ordinates. To put I into the equivalent integral with limits $(-1, 1)$, we note that the midpoint of our interval is $\pi/2$ and our scale factor is also $\pi/2$. Hence our five abscissas will be

$$\frac{\pi}{2}, \quad \frac{\pi}{2}\left(\pm \frac{.53846931\pi}{2}\right), \quad \frac{\pi}{2}\left(\pm \frac{.90617984\pi}{2}\right)$$

or 1.5707963, 1.5707963 $\pm$ .8458356, 1.5707963 $\pm$ 1.4234340 radians.

$$I = \frac{\pi}{2} \left[.56888889 + (2)(.47862867)(\sin .7349707)\right.$$

$$\left. + (2)(.23692689)(\sin .1473723)\right]$$

$$= \frac{\pi}{2}(.56888889 + .63477027 + .06958042)$$

$$= 2.0000000$$

The principal advantage of the Gaussian quadrature over a Newton-Cotes formula is that considerably greater accuracy is obtainable, or equivalently, that the same accuracy is obtainable with about half as many points used.

For *hand computation*, the saving is nonexistent. The integrand must be evaluated at irrational abscissas, which makes the computation about as laborious as if we used the greater number of equally spaced values required by the Newton-Cotes formula of comparable accuracy. In addition there is the necessity of transforming the integral so that the limits are $(-1, 1)$.

For *machine calculation*, these arguments do not hold, particularly where an analytic expression for the integrand is known, or where the integrand is generated by a subroutine of sufficient accuracy. Since digital computer evaluates a function for an irrational argument about as easily as for a rational one, the Gaussian method is attaining the popularity it deserves, and should be used when feasible.

In general, it should *not* be used if the integrand is available only in the form of equally spaced tabular points, for this would require some interpolation formula in the case of the irrational abscissas, so we might just as well use directly the Newton-Cotes formula of the same accuracy as the interpolation formula that would have been used.

PROBLEMS

The following integrals can be evaluated by

(a) The trapezoidal rule.
(b) Simpson's rule.
(c) Boole's rule.
(d) Weddle's rule.
(e) Gaussian quadrature.

The answers supplied were calculated by Gaussian quadrature with $n = 5$.

1. $\int_1^5 \sqrt{1 + x^4}\, dx = 41.71$

2. $\int_1^3 e^{-x^2}\, dx = .1394$

3. $\int_1^4 \frac{dx}{\sqrt{1 + x^3}} = .8959$

4. $\int_0^2 \frac{x\, dx}{\sqrt{1 + x}} = 1.333$

5. $\int_2^6 (1 + x^3)^{3/2} = 3504$

6. $\int_3^6 \sqrt{1 + \cos^2 x}\, dx = 3.622$

7. $\int_1^3 \sqrt{1 + \sin^2 x}\, dx = 2.554$

8. $\int_2^8 \frac{x\, dx}{1 + \ln x} = 11.43$

9. $\int_0^2 \sqrt{1 + x^3}\, dx = 3.241$

10. $\int_0^1 \cos(x^2)\, dx = .9045$

11. $\int_0^{\pi/3} \sqrt{\cos x}\, dx = .9480$

12. $\int_0^{1/2} \frac{x\, dx}{\cos x} = .1334$

13. $\int_1^4 \frac{\sin x}{x}\, dx = .8121$

14. $\int_0^{.2} \frac{e^x}{2 - x}\, dx = .1168$

15. $\int_0^1 \frac{\cos x}{1 + x}\, dx = .6010$

16. $\int_0^1 \frac{dx}{\sqrt[3]{1 + x^2}} = .9181$

17. $\int_0^{.4} \frac{dx}{\sqrt{1 - \sin x}} = .4498$

18. $\int_0^{.9} \frac{dx}{\sqrt[3]{1 - x^2}} = 1.035$

19. $\int_0^{.9} \sqrt[3]{1 - x^2}\, dx = .7979$

20. $\int_0^2 \frac{x\, dx}{\sqrt[3]{1 + x^3}} = 1.1374774$

REFERENCES

HOUSEHOLDER, ALSTON S., *Principles of Numerical Analysis*. New York: McGraw-Hill Book Company, 1953.

MILNE, W. E., *Numerical Calculus*. Princeton, N.J.: Princeton University Press, 1950.

TODD, JOHN, editor, *Survey of Numerical Analysis*. New York: McGraw-Hill Book Company, 1962.

7 SOLUTION OF DIFFERENTIAL EQUATIONS

7.1 INTRODUCTION

The solution of differential equations by digital computer does not give a solution of the nature that an analytic approach would yield. That is, it does not yield the general solution but instead a set of points which lie close to a particular solution of the equation.

We will first consider solution of equations of the type $y' = f(x, y)$ with an initial condition that when $x = x_0$, $y = y_0$. (See Fig. 7.1.) This in terms of analytic solution determines the member of the family of solution curves which is desired (in other words, the constant of integration). We advance the solution in the x direction by incrementing x by h and predicting or extrapolating

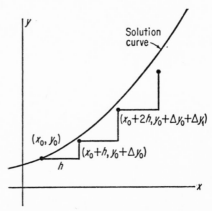

Fig. 7.1.

to a new point $(x_0 + h, y_0 + \Delta y_0)$. This new point is then considered again as a point (x_0, y_0) and the procedure is iterated. Errors tend to accumulate and cause our solution to recede from the analytic solution. Various techniques for minimizing this phenomenon will be covered.

7.2 THE EULER METHOD

In the solution of the equation $y' = f(x, y)$ with the initial condition that $y = y_0$ when $x = x_0$ we can find a new point (x_{n+1}, y_{n+1}) by making use of the definition of the derivative

$$y' = \lim_{\Delta x \to 0} \frac{\Delta y}{\Delta x}$$

Here we approximate y' by $\Delta y / \Delta x$—that is, let

$$y' = \frac{\Delta y}{\Delta x} \tag{7.1}$$

$$y_{n+1} = y_n + \Delta y \tag{7.2}$$

and

$$\Delta y = hy' \quad \text{where } h = \Delta x$$

Now

$$y_{n+1} = y_n + hy_n' \tag{7.3}$$

Also we note that (7.3) is equivalent to the Taylor series truncated after the first derivative term.

EXAMPLE. Solve $y' = xy$ with initial conditions $x_0 = 0$, $y_0 = 1$, and $h = .1$.

Solution.

n	x_n	y_n	y_n'	hy_n'	Analytic solution to eight figures
0	0	1	0	0	1.0000000
1	.1	1	.1	.01	1.0050125
2	.2	1.01	.202	.0202	1.0202013
3	.3	1.0302	.30906	.030906	1.0460283
4	.4	1.061106			1.0832890

The Euler method is not held in high regard for obvious reasons! We include it merely to illustrate the results of errors mentioned in the next section.

7.3 ERRORS IN THE SOLUTION BY DIGITAL COMPUTER

There are three types of errors in the solution of differential equations by any technique other than an analytic solution of the equations. These types are:

I. *Round-off error*. This is machine-made and is caused by the limitations of the particular computer. If we compute using eight digits in multiplication, we would expect by hand calculation 16 digits. The computer retains only the most significant eight of these. In any method there is this type of error. If it were actually rounded this error would be minimized, but rounding is not done.

II. *Truncation error*. With the truncation of a series after only a few terms we are committing a generally known error. This error is not machine-caused but is due to the method.

III. *Propagation or inherited error*. This is caused by the use of previous points calculated by the computer which already are erroneous owing to the two errors above. Since we are already off the solution curve, we cannot expect any new points we compute to be on the correct solution curve. Adding the round-off errors and truncation errors into the calculation causes further errors.

7.4 THE MODIFIED EULER METHOD

Given the initial-value problem $y' = f(x, y)$ with the condition that $y = y_0$ when $x = x_0$, we will truncate the Taylor series after the second derivative term.

$$y = y_0 + y_0'(x - x_0) + \frac{y_0''(x - x_0)^2}{2!} + \cdots \tag{7.4}$$

and

$$y_1 = y_0 + y_0'(x_1 - x_0) + \frac{y_0''(x_1 - x_0)^2}{2}$$

Since $h = x_1 - x_0$ we may write

$$y_1 = y_0 + hy_0' + \frac{h^2}{2} y_0'' \tag{7.5}$$

Recalling forward differences, $\Delta y_0' = y_1' - y_0'$ and an approximation for $y_0'' = (y_1' - y_0')/h$. Replacing the second derivative in (7.5), we have

$$y_1 = y_0 + hy_0' + \frac{h^2}{2} \left[\frac{y_1' + y_0'}{h} \right]$$

or, upon simplification,

$$y_1 = y_0 + \frac{h}{2} [y_0' + y_1'] \tag{7.6}$$

In order to use (7.6) we must have a value for y_1', which requires that we know y_1, which of course we can approximate by $y_1 = y_0 + hy_0'$ (Euler's method). Now we can find $y_1' = f(x_1, y_1)$ and substitute into (7.6). This may be iterated if desirable. The general form is

$$y_{n+1} = y_n + \frac{h}{2}[y'_n + \bar{y}'_{n+1}]$$

where

$$\bar{y}'_{n+1} = f(x_{n+1}, \bar{y}_{n+1})$$
$$\bar{y}_{n+1} = y_n + hy'_n \tag{7.7}$$

EXAMPLE. Solve $y' = xy$ by the modified Euler method. The initial condition is $x = 0$, $y = 1$. Use $h = .1$.

Solution.

n	x_n	y_n	y'_n	hy'_n	$\bar{y}_{n+1}$	$\bar{y}'_{n+1}$	$h\bar{y}'_{n+1}$
0	0	1	0	0	1	.1	.01
1	.1	1.005		.01005	1.01505	.20301	
2	.2	1.0201755					
3	.3	1.0459859					
4	.4	1.0832229					
5	.5	1.1330511					
6	.6	1.1970684					

The analytic solution at $x = .6$ is $y = 1.1972281$.

Many times the modified Euler method will not give as good results as these. The method has been used to simulate an integrator used in analog computation on a digital computer, as the analog computer accuracy is not within 2 to 3 per cent. However, extended use of the modified Euler method could be disastrous.

7.5 THE RUNGE-KUTTA METHOD

This method is similar in derivation to the modified Euler method but more terms of the series are used. In fact, this version of the Runge-Kutta method uses terms through the fourth derivative. The equations are given below:

$$y_{n+1} = y_n + \tfrac{1}{6}[k_1 + 2k_2 + 2k_3 + k_4] \tag{7.8}$$

where

$$k_1 = hf(x_n, y_n) \tag{7.9}$$

$$k_2 = hf(x_n + \tfrac{1}{2}h, y_n + \tfrac{1}{2}k_1) \tag{7.10}$$

$$k_3 = hf(x_n + \tfrac{1}{2}h, y_n + \tfrac{1}{2}k_2) \tag{7.11}$$

$$k_4 = hf(x_n + h, y_n + k_3) \tag{7.12}$$

The differential equation must, of course, be written as $y' = f(x, y)$ with an initial condition that $x = x_0$ when $y = y_0$.

[It is interesting to note that if the equation is of the form $y' = f(x)$—that is, $f(x, y)$ is free of the dependent variable—the Runge-Kutta method reduces to a form of Simpson's rule.]

The use of the Runge-Kutta method is as follows: Compute the four k values from (7.9), (7.10), (7.11), and (7.12) and substitute into (7.8). This yields a new point (x_{n+1}, y_{n+1}), which is then reused as the initial point. This process is repeated across the interval of the desired solution.

EXAMPLE. Solve $y' = x - y$ for the initial condition $x = 0$, $y = 2$ with $h = .1$.

Solution.

$x_0 = 0$, $y_0 = 2$, $h = .1$, $y' = x - y$

$k_1 = .1(0 - 2) = -.2$

$k_2 = .1\{.05 - [2 + \tfrac{1}{2}(-.2)]\} = .1[.05 - 1.9] = -.185$

$k_3 = .1\{.05 - [2 + \tfrac{1}{2}(-.185)]\} = .1[.05 - 1.9075]$

$\quad = .1[-1.8575] = -.18575$

$k_4 = .1\{.1 - (2 - .18575)\} = .1[.1 - 1.81425] = -.171425$

$y_1 = 2 + \tfrac{1}{6}[-.2 + 2(-.185) + 2(-.18575) - .171425] = 1.8145125$

Now, using $x = .1$ and $y = 1.8145125$ as the initial point,

$$k_1 = -.17145125$$

$$k_2 = -1.5787869$$

$$k_3 = -1.5855732$$

$$k_4 = 1.4559552$$

$$y_2 = 1.6561927$$

Now

$x_2 = .2$,	$y_2 = 1.6561927$
$x_3 = .3$,	$y_3 = 1.5224553$
$x_4 = .4$,	$y_4 = 1.4109609$
$x_5 = .5$,	$y_5 = 1.3195929$
$x_6 = .6$,	$y_6 = 1.2464359$

7.6 MILNE'S METHOD

In Section 6.2 we derived Simpson's rule, which can be written as

$$\int_{x_{n-1}}^{x_{n+1}} y \, dx = \frac{h}{3} [y_{n-1} + 4y_n + y_{n+1}] \tag{7.13}$$

If we replace y by y' in (7.13), the value of the resulting integral can be immediately written down, and we have

$$y_{n+1} = y_{n-1} + \frac{h}{3} [y'_{n-1} + 4y'_n + y'_{n+1}] - \frac{1}{90} h^5 y^{(v)}(\bar{x}) \tag{7.14}$$

Note that in order to use equation (7.14) to compute y_{n+1}, we must already know y'_{n+1}, which of course requires that we know y_{n+1}. Obviously we must have a way to find y'_{n+1}. In this situation we predict a value for y_{n+1} by the following formula:

$$y_{n+1} = y_{n-3} + \frac{4h}{3} (2y'_n - y'_{n-1} + 2y'_{n-2}) + \frac{28}{90} h^5 y^{(v)}(\bar{x}) \tag{7.15}$$

This formula can be derived by undetermined coefficients. The last terms in equations (7.14) and (7.15) are error terms which may be used to control the program and the step size. Note that (7.15) requires four previously computed points. These points may be computed by the Runge-Kutta method of the previous section.

The use of these formulas is as follows:

(1) Compute the necessary starting values by the Runge-Kutta method.

(2) Compute y_{n+1} using equation (7.15) (which is frequently called the predictor).

(3) Compute y_{n+1} using (7.14) with the use of the predicted value for y_{n+1} from step two. (This step may be iterated.)

(4) Check on the error terms; if they are too large, reduce the step size and compute new values with the new step size by the Runge-Kutta method; if the error terms are very small, increase the step size; otherwise continue to the next point by repeating steps beginning with step two.

One may wonder why we need bother with the corrector at all. The answer is, of course, related to the accuracy obtainable. The error term of the predictor is given by $\frac{28}{90} h^5 y^{(v)}(\xi_1)$ where ξ_1 lies between x_{n-3} and x_{n+1}. For the corrector, the error term is $-\frac{1}{90} h^5 y^{(v)}(\xi_2)$. (The error is added to the computed value to obtain the true value.)

EXAMPLE. As before, we seek the solution of $y' = x - y$ passing through $(0, 2)$, with a step size of 0.1. We assume that the values on the lines $n = 1$,

2, 3 have been obtained by the Runge-Kutta method. Then Milne's method is used to advance the solution to x_4 and x_5.

n	x_n	y_n	y'_n	D
0	.0	2.0	-2.0	
1	.1	1.814512	-1.714512	
2	.2	1.656192	-1.456192	
3	.3	1.522455	-1.222455	
4	.4	1.410968	-1.010968	
		1.410959	-1.010959	-9
		1.410960	-1.010960	
5	.5	1.319599	$-.819599$	
		1.319592	$-.819592$	-7

We have computed y_4 and y_5, which agree in all digits with the analytic solution. The calculation proceeds from left to right. 1.410968 is the value obtained for y_4 by use of (7.15). In all cases y'_n is found by $y'_n = x_n - y_n$. The first use of (7.14) gives $y_4 = 1.410959$, the second gives 1.410960. The values in the D column represent the correction (in the last decimal place) that the first use of (7.14) provides. This column provides a check on accidental computational errors, which will show up as a large change in D. More important is its use as an indicator of the appropriateness of the step size.

If accuracy such as this is so readily attainable, it would seem that Milne's method would be ideal. The fact is that it is *not* often used *on automatic digital computers*. One reason, of course, is that the need for a separate starting procedure lengthens the program required. A much more important reason is that Milne's method is inherently *unstable*, in that the propagated error may grow exponentially.

The value of $D/29$ gives an estimate of the truncation error introduced in each step, but says nothing about how previously introduced error is propagated. This can be very serious on a typical problem run on a digital computer, where the high speed may make problems that involve even thousands of small steps not unreasonably long.

7.7 ADAMS-BASHFORTH METHOD

We can avoid the instability of Milne's method by using different formulas for the predictor and corrector. One such set of formulas is the Adams-Bashforth method. We will derive the predictor.

From previous work we recall the shifting operator E, which when applied to y_n yields y_{n+1} or $Ey_n = y_{n+1}$. When applied to $y(x)$ as $Ey(x)$ it yields the next y, or y when x is replaced by $x + h$. Hence $Ey(x) = y(x + h)$.

Proceeding formally,

$$Ey(x) = y(x + h) = y(x) + hy'(x) + \frac{h^2}{2!} y''(x)$$

$$+ \frac{h^3}{3!} y'''(x) + \cdots + \frac{h^n}{n!} y^{(n)}(x) \qquad (7.16)$$

This can be written as follows, using the differential operator D:

$$Ey(x) = \left(1 + hD + \frac{h^2 D^2}{2!} + \frac{h^3 D^3}{3!} + \frac{h^4 D^4}{4!} + \cdots + \frac{h^n D^{(n)}}{n!} + \cdots \right) y(x)$$

$$(7.17)$$

Immediately we recognize that

$$\left(1 + hD + \frac{h^2 D^2}{2!} + \frac{h^3 D^3}{3!} + \frac{h^4 D^4}{4!} + \cdots + \frac{h^n D^{(n)}}{n!} \right) = e^{hD}$$

So we have from (7.17)

$$Ey(x) = e^{hD} y(x)$$

Formally we may write $E = e^{hD}$.

Another identity involving E is $\nabla = 1 - E^{-1}$ where ∇ is the backward difference operator. Again we may write $E = 1/(1 - \nabla)$ by suitable algebraic manipulation. By long division

$$E = \frac{1}{1 - \nabla} = 1 + \nabla + \nabla^2 + \nabla^3 + \nabla^4 + \nabla^5 + \nabla^6 + \cdots + \nabla^n + \cdots \qquad (7.18)$$

Since $E = e^{hD}$, we may write $hD = \ln E = \ln[1/(1 - \nabla)]$, or by Taylor series expansion about $\nabla = 0$ we have

$$hD = \ln\left(\frac{1}{1 - \nabla}\right) = -\ln(1 - \nabla)$$

$$= \nabla + \frac{\nabla^2}{2} + \frac{\nabla^3}{3} + \frac{\nabla^4}{4} + \frac{\nabla^5}{5} + \frac{\nabla^6}{6} + \cdots + \frac{\nabla^n}{n} + \cdots \qquad (7.19)$$

Now

$$\nabla E = \nabla(1 + \nabla + \nabla^2 + \nabla^3 + \nabla^4 + \nabla^5 + \nabla^6 + \cdots + \nabla^n)$$

$$hD = \left(\nabla + \frac{\nabla^2}{2} + \frac{\nabla^3}{3} + \frac{\nabla^4}{4} + \frac{\nabla^5}{5} + \frac{\nabla^6}{6} + \frac{\nabla^7}{7} + \cdots + \frac{\nabla^n}{n} \right)$$

$$\frac{\nabla E}{hD} = \frac{\nabla(1 + \nabla + \nabla^2 + \nabla^3 + \nabla^4 + \nabla^5 + \nabla^6 + \cdots + \nabla^n)}{\left(\nabla + \dfrac{\nabla^2}{2} + \dfrac{\nabla^3}{3} + \dfrac{\nabla^4}{4} + \dfrac{\nabla^5}{5} + \dfrac{\nabla^6}{6} + \dfrac{\nabla^7}{7} + \cdots + \dfrac{\nabla^n}{n} + \cdots \right)}$$

and by division

$$\frac{\nabla E}{hD} = \left(1 + \frac{1}{2}\nabla + \frac{5}{12}\nabla^2 + \frac{3}{8}\nabla^3 + \frac{251}{720}\nabla^4 + \cdots\right)$$

or

$$\nabla E = \left(1 + \frac{1}{2}\nabla + \frac{5}{12}\nabla^2 + \frac{3}{8}\nabla^3 + \frac{251}{720}\nabla^4 + \cdots\right)hD$$

Operating on y_n by the operator ∇E, we have

$$\nabla E y_n = \left(1 + \frac{1}{2}\nabla + \frac{5}{12}\nabla^2 + \frac{3}{8}\nabla^3 + \frac{251}{720}\nabla^4 + \cdots\right)hDy_n$$

or

$$\nabla y_{n+1} = y_{n+1} - y_n = h\left(1 + \frac{1}{2}\nabla + \frac{5}{12}\nabla^2 + \frac{3}{8}\nabla^3 + \frac{251}{720}\nabla^4 + \cdots\right)Dy_n$$

and $Dy_n = y_n'$. Now we have

$$y_{n+1} = y_n + h\left(1 + \frac{1}{2}\nabla + \frac{5}{12}\nabla^2 + \frac{3}{8}\nabla^3 + \frac{251}{720}\nabla^4 + \cdots\right)y_n'$$

or

$$y_{n+1} = y_n + h\left[y_n' + \frac{1}{2}\nabla y_n' + \frac{5}{12}\nabla^2 y_n' + \frac{3}{8}\nabla^3 y_n'\right] + h\frac{251}{720}\nabla^4 y_n'$$

By substituting

$$\nabla y_n' = y_n' - y_{n-1}'$$
$$\nabla^2 y_n' = y_n' - 2y_{n-1}' + y_{n-2}'$$
$$\nabla^3 y_n' = y_n' - 3y_{n-1}' + 3y_{n-2}' - y_{n-3}'$$

and combining terms using $\frac{251}{720}h^5 y_n'$ as an error term, we have

$$y_{n+1} = y_n + \frac{h}{24}[55y_n' - 59y_{n-1}' + 37y_{n-2}' - 9y_{n-3}'] + \frac{251}{720}h^5 y^{(5)} \quad (7.20)$$

The last term is the error term and is carried along to judge whether to decrease the step size when it becomes large or to increase the step size when it becomes excessively small.

The corrector formula is

$$y_{n+1} = y_n + \frac{h}{24}[9y_{n+1}' + 19y_n' - 5y_{n-1}' + y_{n-2}'] \quad (7.21)$$

with an error term of $-\frac{19}{720}h^5 y^5$. The derivation of the corrector is similar to the derivation of the predictor and is, therefore, not presented here.

This method proceeds just as does Milne's. Having four starting values, we advance the solution from x_n to x_{n+1} by applying the predictor (7.20) to get a tentative $y_{n+1}^{(1)}$, finding y_{n+1}' from the given differential equation. then applying (7.21) iteratively until the solution converges. Again, it would be advantageous to know when a *single* application of (7.21) is sufficient. The rule here is that when (7.20) and the first use of (7.21) give results that differ by less than 7 units (in the last decimal place retained), the truncation error for this step is probably less than $\frac{1}{2}$ unit.

We note that the accuracy of a single step by this method is approximately that of Milne's method, as can be seen by comparing the error terms. Of great practical importance is the fact that an error introduced at one stage in the Adams-Bashforth procedure does *not* tend to grow exponentially thereafter. Since organization of the work is so similar for the two methods, no numerical example will be given here.

7.8 SIMULTANEOUS EQUATIONS

Suppose we have

$$\frac{dy}{dx} = f(x, y, z)$$

$$\frac{dz}{dx} = g(x, y, z)$$

Then the solutions are given by the Runge-Kutta method as follows:

$$y_{n+1} = y_n + \tfrac{1}{6}(k_1 + 2k_2 + 2k_3 + k_4)$$

$$z_{n+1} = z_n + \tfrac{1}{6}(m_1 + 2m_2 + 2m_3 + m_4)$$

where

$$k_1 = hf(x_n, y_n, z_n)$$

$$k_2 = hf(x_n + \tfrac{1}{2}h, y_n + \tfrac{1}{2}k_1, z_n + \tfrac{1}{2}m_1)$$

$$k_3 = hf(x_n + \tfrac{1}{2}h, y_n + \tfrac{1}{2}k_2, z_n + \tfrac{1}{2}m_2)$$

$$k_4 = hf(x_n + h, y_n + k_3, z_n + m_3)$$

and

$$m_1 = hg(x_n, y_n, z_n)$$

$$m_2 = hg(x_n + \tfrac{1}{2}h, y_n + \tfrac{1}{2}k_1, z_n + \tfrac{1}{2}m_1)$$

$$m_3 = hg(x_n + \tfrac{1}{2}h, y_n + \tfrac{1}{2}k_2, z_n + \tfrac{1}{2}m_2)$$

$$m_4 = hg(x_n + h, y_n + k_3, z_n + m_3)$$

We see that the k_i and m_i are to be computed in the order k_1, m_1, k_2, m_2, and so on. The Milne or Adams-Bashforth methods may also be used in a similar fashion.

7.9   NYSTROM SCHEME FOR SECOND-ORDER (INITIAL-VALUE) EQUATIONS

Instead of using the Runge-Kutta method for second-order equations, the following result due to E. J. Nystrom may be used directly. The work follows the same pattern as Runge-Kutta itself. The form $y'' = f(x, y, y')$ is appropriate for the Nystrom method, and x, y, y' values at an initial point must be known.

$$y'' = f(x, y, y')$$

$$y_{m+1} = y_m + hy_m' + \frac{h^2(f_1 + f_2 + f_3)}{6} \tag{7.22}$$

$$y_{m+1}' = y_m' + \frac{h(f_1 + 2f_2 + 2f_3 + f_4)}{16} \tag{7.23}$$

$$f_1 = f(x_m, y_m, y_m')$$

$$f_2 = f\left(x_m + \frac{h}{2}, y_m + \frac{hy_m'}{2} + \frac{h^2 f_1}{8}, y_m' + \frac{hf_1}{3}\right)$$

$$f_3 = f\left(x_m + \frac{h}{2}, y_m + \frac{hy_m'}{2} + \frac{h^2 f_1}{8}, y_m' + \frac{hf_2}{2}\right)$$

$$f_4 = f\left(x_m + h, y_m + hy_m' + \frac{h^2 f_3}{2}, y_m' + hf_3\right)$$

The quantities f_i are computed first and substituted into (7.22) and (7.23), after which the next point is ready for calculation. Error analysis of this method is very tedious in the general case.

7.10   FOURTH-ORDER EQUATIONS

A similar process for fourth-order equations is due to R. Zurmuhl and is written as follows:

$$y^{(4)} = f(x, y) \tag{7.24}$$

$$y_{m+1} = y_m + hy_m' + \frac{h^2 y_m''}{2} + \frac{h^3 y_m'''}{6} + \frac{h^4(8f_1 + 4f_2 + 4f_3 - f_4)}{360} \tag{7.25}$$

$$y_{m+1}' = y_m' + hy_m'' + \frac{h^2 y_m'''}{2} + \frac{h^3(9f_1 + 6f_2 + 6f_3 - f_4)}{120} \tag{7.26}$$

$$y''_{m+1} = y''_m + hy'''_m + \frac{h^2(f_1 + f_2 + f_3)}{6} \tag{7.27}$$

$$y'''_{m+1} = y'''_m + \frac{h(f_1 + 2f_2 + 2f_3 + f_4)}{6} \tag{7.28}$$

$$f_1 = f(x_m, y_m)$$

$$f_2 = f_3 = f\left(x_m + \frac{h}{2}, y_m + \frac{hy'_m}{2} + \frac{h^2 y''_m}{8} + \frac{h^3 y'''_m}{48} + \frac{h^4 f_1}{384}\right)$$

$$f_4 = f\left(x_m + h, y_m + hy'_m + \frac{h^2 y''_m}{2} + \frac{h^3 y'''_m}{6} + \frac{h^4 f_3}{24}\right)$$

As with Runge-Kutta and Nystrom, the f_i are computed first and substituted into (7.25), (7.26), (7.27), (7.28).

PROBLEMS

The following initial-value problems may be solved by the Euler, modified Euler, Runge-Kutta, Milne, and Adams-Bashforth methods. For the Milne and Adams-Bashforth methods the necessary starting points may be generated by the Runge-Kutta method. Answers are given for one point for each problem after several steps. (Answers computed by Runge-Kutta.)

1. $y' = \dfrac{y - x}{x + y}$ with $x_0 = 0$, $y_0 = 1$, $h = .1$.

[*Ans.* When $x = 2.$, $y = 1.5196908$.]

2. $y' = \dfrac{x + y}{10e^x}$ with $x_0 = 0$, $y_0 = 5.$, $h = .1$.

[*Ans.* When $x = 2.$, $y = 5.5124692$.]

3. $y' - \sin xy = 0$ with $x_0 = 0$, $y_0 = .5$, $h = .1$.

[*Ans.* When $x = 2.$, $y = 1.5357207$.]

4. $10xy' + y^2 - 2 = 0$ with $x_0 = 4$, $y_0 = 1.$, $h = .1$.

[*Ans.* When $x = 6.$, $y = 1.0389245$.]

5. $y' + y^2 = e^x$ with $x_0 = 0$, $y_0 = 1$, $h = .1$.

[*Ans.* When $x = 2.1$, $y = 2.5944027$.]

6. $x^2 y' + xy - 1 = 0$ with $x_0 = 1$, $y_0 = 1$, $h = .1$.

[*Ans.* When $x = 3.$, $y = .69953757$.]

The following problem may be solved by the simultaneous-equations techniques.

7. $dy/dx = 6x - 3z - 5$, $dz/dx = (x - y + 5)/3$, with $x_0 = 0$, $y_0 = 2$, $z_0 = -1$, $h = .1$.

[*Ans.* When $x = .5$, $y = 1.31959$, $z = -0.393469$; $x = 1.$, $y = 1.10364$, $z = .367880$.]

REFERENCES

MILNE, W. E., *Numerical Solution of Differential Equations.* New York: John Wiley & Sons, Inc., 1953.

SCARBOROUGH, J. B., *Numerical Mathematical Analysis*, 3rd ed. Baltimore: Johns Hopkins Press, 1955.

HILDEBRAND, F. B., *Introduction to Numerical Analysis.* New York: McGraw-Hill Book Company, 1956.

8 A SIMPLE BOUNDARY-VALUE PROBLEM

8.1 INTRODUCTION

We have heretofore considered only differential equations with initial conditions. When conditions are imposed on the solution at *both* end points of the interval in which the solution is to be found, the problem is less amenable to a numerical approach. A method of successive approximation may be attempted.

The simplest example of a boundary-value problem is $y'' = f(x, y, y')$ over the interval (a, b), with $y = y_a$ at $x = a$ and $y = y_b$ at $x = b$. One solution method is to assume a value p_1 for the derivative y' at $x_0 = a$, then integrate the differential equation by a step-by-step method to $x = b$. The departure of the computed $y(b)$ from y_b will give some idea of a better starting value p_2 for y_0'. From this a new $y(b)$ is computed, and by judicious interpolation we may approach rather close to the true solution after a number of trials.

The method is computer time-consuming. The work can be shortened by using at first integration formulas of low accuracy, or by taking large steps, refining the calculations only when relatively near the final solution.

8.2 DIFFERENCE EQUATIONS

A more useful method involves replacing derivatives by corresponding differences. This is frequently done when the equation is linear in y and its derivatives. The first derivative y' is approximated by

$$y_i' = \frac{1}{2h}(\Delta + \nabla)y_i$$

where h is the width of a subinterval of the interval (a, b). Simplifying,

$$y'_i = \frac{1}{2h}(\Delta + \nabla)y_i = \frac{1}{2h}(y_{i+1} - y_i + y_i - y_{i-1})$$

$$y'_i = \frac{y_{i+1} - y_{i-1}}{2h} \tag{8.1}$$

In a similar fashion y''_i is approximated by

$$y''_i = \frac{1}{h^2}\delta^2 y_i \tag{8.2}$$

Central differences are similar to forward differences and have the following definitions:

$$\delta y_i = y_{i+(1/2)} - y_{i-(1/2)} \tag{8.3}$$

$$\delta^2 y_i = \delta(\delta y_i) = \delta(y_{i+(1/2)} - y_{i-(1/2)}) = \delta y_{i+(1/2)} - \delta y_{i-(1/2)}$$

$$= y_{i+1} - y_i - (y_i - y_{i-1}) = y_{i+1} - 2y_i + y_{i-1} \tag{8.4}$$

So that by equation (8.4)

$$y''_i = \frac{1}{h^2}(y_{i+1} - 2y_i + y_{i-1}) \tag{8.5}$$

Now the equation $y'' = f(x, y, y')$ is replaced by the corresponding difference equation

$$\frac{y_{i+1} - 2y_i + y_{i-1}}{h^2} = f\left(x_i, y_i, \frac{y_{i+1} - y_{i-1}}{2h}\right)$$

or for computing purposes

$$y_{i+1} - 2y_i + y_{i-1} = h^2 f\left(x_i, y_i, \frac{y_{i+1} - y_{i-1}}{2h}\right) \tag{8.6}$$

Equation (8.6) is to hold for $i = 1, 2, 3, \ldots, n - 1$ since we have divided the interval (a, b) into n subintervals of width h. These equations will be linear in the y_i when the differential equation is linear in y and its derivatives. For this case there are solutions available via matrix techniques.

EXAMPLE. Approximate the solution of the problem $y'' + y = 0$ with the conditions that when $x = 0$, $y = 0$ and when $x = 1$, $y = 1$ by using equation (8.6).

Solution. First using $n = 2$, the "system" of linear equations becomes one equation:

$$y_2 - 2y_1 + y_0 = -(.5)^2(y_1)$$

Now $y_2 = 1$ and $y_0 = 0$ so that we have $1 - 2y_1 = -.25y_1$ or $1.75y_1 = 1$, $y_1 = .57143$. This is the approximation to the point where $x = .5$. The analytic solution of the equation is $y = \sin x/\sin 1$ so that when $x = .5$, $y = .5941$. This is at least a ball-park approximation.

Now let us use $n = 4$ so that we approximate values of y for $x = .25$, $.50, .75$ using $h = .25$. Now the equations are

$$y_2 - 2y_1 + y_0 = -(.25)^2 y_1$$
$$y_3 - 2y_2 + y_1 = -(.25)^2 y_2$$
$$y_4 - 2y_3 + y_2 = -(.25)^2 y_3$$

and $y_0 = 0$ but $y_4 = 1$ so that we have

$$y_2 - 1.9375y_1 = 0$$
$$y_3 - 1.9375y_2 + y_1 = 0$$
$$- 1.9375y_3 + y_2 = - 1$$

Solving these we obtain for $x = .25, .50, .75$

$$y_1 = .29493$$
$$y_2 = .57143$$
$$y_3 = .812210$$

Likewise let us write the equations for $n = 5$ and $h = .2$:

$$y_0 - 2y_1 + y_2 = -.04y_1$$
$$y_1 - 2y_2 + y_3 = -.04y_2$$
$$y_2 - 2y_3 + y_4 = -.04y_3$$
$$y_3 - 2y_4 + y_5 = -.04y_4$$

Since $y_0 = 0$ and $y_5 = 1$, the equations simplify to the following

$$-1.96y_1 + \quad y_2 = 0$$
$$y_1 - 1.96y_2 + \quad y_3 = 0$$
$$y_2 - 1.96y_3 + \quad y_4 = 0$$
$$y_3 - 1.96y_4 = -1$$

The solutions of these equations are:

$$y_1 = .2360$$
$$y_2 = .4627$$
$$y_3 = .6709$$
$$y_4 = .8522 \quad (\sin 1 = .8415)$$

The solutions (to four figures) by the analytic solution for $x = .2, .4, .6, .8$ are

$$y_2 = .2376$$

$$y_4 = .4626$$

$$y_6 = .6708$$

$$y_8 = .8524$$

Using $n = 10$, the equations are

$$0 - 1.99y_1 + y_2 = 0$$

$$y_1 - 1.99y_2 + y_3 = 0$$

$$y_2 - 1.99y_3 + y_4 = 0$$

$$y_3 - 1.99y_4 + y_5 = 0$$

$$y_4 - 1.99y_5 + y_6 = 0$$

$$y_5 - 1.99y_6 + y_7 = 0$$

$$y_6 - 1.99y_7 + y_8 = 0$$

$$y_7 - 1.99y_8 + y_9 = 0$$

$$y_8 - 1.99y_9 + 1 = 0$$

And the solutions are

x	y_i	Analytic solution
.1	.1186	.1186
.2	.2361	.2361
.3	.3512	.3512
.4	.4628	.4628
.5	.5698	.5697
.6	.6711	.6710
.7	.7656	.7656
.8	.8521	.8525
.9	.9304	.9309

Note that the deviation of the y_i from the analytic solution increases at the bottom of the table. This is an example of the accumulation of round-off errors. y_1 was calculated first and substituted into the other equations in order.

PROBLEMS

1. Solve $y'' = x - y$ with boundary conditions when $x = 0$, $y = 0$ and when $x = 1$, $y = 2$. Use $h = .2$.
   The analytic solutions are

x	y
.2	.51207
.4	1.0117
.6	1.4867
.8	1.9267

2. Solve $y'' + y = x$ with boundary conditions $x(0) = 0$, $x(1) = 1$.

3. Solve $y'' - 5y' + 6y = \sin x$ with boundary conditions $x(0) = 0$, $x(\pi/2) = 0$.

INDEX